Dr. Schindler's

Woman's Guide to Better Living

52 Weeks a Year

Dr. Schindler's
Woman's Guide

Englewood Cliffs, N.J.

to Better Living

52 Weeks a Year

by **JOHN A. SCHINDLER, M.D.**

Member of the Department of Medicine
The Monroe Clinic, Monroe, Wisconsin

PRENTICE-HALL, INC., 1957

PRINTED IN THE UNITED STATES OF AMERICA

21862

To
Dorothea

Contents

❧ ❧ ❧

vii

1. **A Predictably Pleasant Disposition and How to Acquire It (Continued)**

   Dispositions Are Unpredictable and Often Disagreeable. Is the Individual with a Steady, Good Disposition Uninspiring and Insipid? The Impulsive, Assertive Disposition Is a Sad and Juvenile Error. What Are Impulses? One of Women's Main Troubles Is the Disposition of Men. Picking a Husband with a Pleasant Disposition. Women's Troubles with Their Own Dispositions. A Good Disposition Is Based on a Philosophy. The Importance to a Woman of a Good Disposition.

2. **A Sense of Humor Adds Spice to Life** . . . .

   A Sense of Humor and a Pleasant Disposition Go Together. The Distinction Between Wit and Humor. Picking the Right Kind of Sense of Humor. Discovering a Sense of "Humor." A General, Over-all Sense of Humor. It's Never Too Late to Acquire a Sense of Humor. A Sense of Humor Is the Houseslave's Salvation. Rubbing Humor Off on the Husband.

3. **Making the Most of It** . . . .

   Why Women Seem Less Mature Than Men in the Matter of Making the Most of It. Geraldine and Henrietta: Victims of Marginal Husbands. The Story of Geraldine and Joe. Henrietta's Marital Frustration with Emil. The Courage to Make the Most of It. How Geraldine and Henrietta Met Their Problems. How Geraldine Found Courage. Henrietta Did Not Find the Way Out. How Many Women Become Chronic Complainers. Loss of Courage May Lead to Reactive Depression. The Earthy Type of Courage. Janet — A Woman of Magnificent Courage.

4. **Meeting Adversity and Being Flexible and Adaptable** .

   I. MEETING ADVERSITY   68

   Lives of Ease vs. Lives of Adversity. "No Life Is so Hard But ..." Conditioning the Maturity of Rising Above Adversity. Teaching Yourself to Meet Adversity. Emotions Are Physical Phenomena. First of All, Accept

4. **Meeting Adversity and Being Flexible and Adaptable**
   (Continued)

   *the Fact. Forming the Sustaining Attitude. Work, an
   Antidote for Adversity. The Strength Afforded by Re-
   ligion in Time of Adversity. Condition Yourself to This
   Maturity.*

   II.   BEING FLEXIBLE AND ADAPTABLE TO CHANGE   77
   Disciplines for Keeping Oneself Flexible and Adaptable.

5. **Being Unselfish and Having Consideration for Others .   84**

   *Women Come by This Maturity More Naturally Than
   Do Men. Which Is the Most Important Maturity? Why
   Children Become Little Selfish Monsters. There Are
   Varying Degrees and Mixtures of Selfishness and Un-
   selfishness in People. Enlightened Selfishness. Consid-
   eration for Others a Part of Enlightened Selfishness.
   Enlightened Selfishness Actually Is the Basis of Our Life.
   Our Lives Absolutely Depend on Others. Selfishness vs.
   Enlightened Selfishness in the Family. The "Pay-Off" of
   Selfish Egoism.*

   I.   GIVING RATHER THAN RECEIVING   100
   Childhood Conditioning in Giving and Receiving.

   II.   CHEATING NO ONE AND STEALING NOTHING   106

6. **Living with Confidence Instead of Fear 108**
   *Fear Is Universal in Human Beings. The Mature Atti-
   tude, Confident Living, Is Developed in the Family.
   Avoiding Fear of Death. Ours Is a Fear Economy. How
   to Get Over Your Fears. How Did the Fear Begin?*

7. **It Is Unnecessary to Be Irritated or Angry 122**
   *Two Adults Who Became Enraged over Tremendous
   Trifles. One Might Expect Two Children to Fight Over
   Nothing. The Absurdity of Anger. The Sad Case of Jane
   and Her Immature Reactions. How the Immaturity of
   Anger Is Conditioned. Anger Is Always Childish and
   Ineffective. Do Not Resort to Angry Discipline with
   Children. Learn to say "Nuts" to Irritations.*

8. **Having a Tenderness and Compassion for Things Human 134**
   *The Greatest Personal Misfortune Is to Be Cruel. Cruelty
   Is the Worst of All Vices. Cruelty a Prominent Feature*

11. **The Factual Basis of Marriage (Continued)**

*The Most Serious Problems Encountered in the Mar-
riages of 818 People. Sexual Relations Are Important in
Making a Marriage a Success or a Failure. The Chances
of Being Happy or Unhappy in Marriage. Women Who
Make a Success of Their Marriage Tend to Have These
Characteristics. Marriage Failure Can Be Traced to
Three Causes in the Large Proportion of Cases. Quarrels
Over Tremendous Trifles. The Family Conference
Method of Settling Problems. Little Change Should Be
Expected After Marriage. Marital Adjustments Require
a Little Time. Above All: Put a Rich Mixture of Com-
mon Sense Into Your Ideals.*

Dr. Schindler's

Woman's Guide to Better Living

52 Weeks a Year

Why Are So Many Women Failures?

꿈̈̈   꿈̈̈   꿈̈̈

I. WHAT IS WRONG WITH WOMEN?

● *What Physicians Learn About Women in Their Offices*

Why are there so very many, *so very many,* women who have developed a condition of frustration in their lives?

We'll have to go into the offices of physicians—of physicians all over the United States—to grasp the picture. In virtually every physician's office, whether he is a general practitioner or a specialist, the picture is essentially the same.

The bulk of medical practice in the United States—50 to 75 per cent of it—is concerned with emotionally induced illness (E.I.I.), a disease that is the physical effect produced by anxious, disturbed, irritated, and unhappy emotions. ——————

And the most astonishing part of this very astonishing picture is that there are three women patients with emotionally induced illness to every man with the same disease! This situation is no secret among doctors. It exists in every medical office.

The significance of this picture is not the emotionally induced illness *per se.* Emotionally induced illness is an indicator of something else far more significant; it indicates a great amount of care, difficulty and trouble in a person's life that is gradually growing intolerable, like a screw being steadily and remorselessly turned tighter. It is an indicator that there is something very rotten somewhere in the woman's "state of Denmark."

What is it? What *is* wrong with women?

This picture in physicians' offices gives us a good reason for asking. But it isn't yet the entire picture. Let us add some more.

1

If you follow the history of all the women in any given area, you will find that roughly 25 per cent of them have a degree of E.I.I. that requires medical care at least once every year through the years. Some of these unfortunate women have E.I.I., in a kaleidoscopic fashion, every day of the year, year in and year out. Another approximate 25 per cent of the total number of women have a major attack of E.I.I. once every five years; another 25 per cent every ten years, and only the remaining 25 per cent do not require medical attention for E.I.I. through the years!

Do you wonder why a doctor asks:

"What is wrong with women?"

We may well ask—*and you women may well ask yourselves* the same question—"What *is* wrong with women?"

Does this situation in the lives of so many women, that is mirrored by the patients in doctors' offices, have something intrinsically to do with the type of life a woman is usually required to lead?

First of all, very definitely, let me say that the frustration in so many women's lives has nothing in the least to do with any weakness that women might have *as* women. As a matter of fact, the idea that women are "The Weaker Sex" has no support in scientific fact. Quite the contrary. There is every evidence that women are biologically more able to stand physical and psychological stress than are men.

● **Are Women the Weaker Sex?**

There has always been a great deal of silly bantering back and forth between the sexes that one is superior to the other. Men, particularly, with the egocentricity that characterizes the male, are ready to claim that they are "superior." This is a delusion men have enjoyed through the years, and it is only recently that scientific investigation has shown that neither sex is innately superior to the other in any significant way. We are finally beginning to understand that the sexes, assuming an ideal social arrangement, would be complementary and virtually equal. Man's avowed superiority is based upon two factors that, in typical masculine fashion, he has maneuvered to the disadvantage of women, and both of which have influenced civilization in directions that have been to its disadvantage.

The first factor in man's "superiority" is that he is superior in sheer physical strength owing to a larger bone and muscle structure. This advantage he has used for years in helping him assume a dominant role. Secondly, being free of the child-bearing function that periodically incapacitates women gives him another advantage that he has exploited.

These two advantages, more than any others, man has used to control things pretty much as he pleases. His control has not been an unmitigated blessing. The very fact that the male characteristics of aggressiveness and pugnacity have become dominant in society, has had much to do in fomenting the wars and the other 57 varieties of conflict that so jeopardize and disturb human living.

There is good evidence that rather than being the weaker, woman has the superior physical *nature*. Her acute strength may not be as great as man's but her endurance at continued physical labor is greater. Physiologically she adjusts more quickly to physical changes in the environment and she can stand untoward conditions longer.

Psychologically she adjusts more readily and rapidly to situational disturbances and can withstand situational stress to a greater degree than can a man.

The female constitution is apparently tougher than the male's. The female fetus has a better chance of being born alive than has the male fetus. The female child has a longer life expectancy than the male, is less plagued with hereditary defects, and is more resistant to disease. A woman can endure pain more stoically and to a greater degree than a man can. Women suffer feeble-mindedness and insanity less often than men; they have fewer neuroses and psychoneuroses.

These qualities in a woman's constitution have offset and complemented man's superior physical strength to some extent, and have also given her certain advantages. For instance, because women tend to outlive their husbands, a great share of the wealth of the country resides in women's hands.

But it is not competitive advantages that the sexes must seek, but the ability to complement each other's qualities to the greater benefit of both.

There is no mental inequality between the sexes. Mentally, as physically, there is no inequality between the sexes. Such differences as there are serve to complement each other.

These differences could be mutually beneficial if men and women were equally active in the working world.

In his mental capacities, the male again tends towards extremes as far as intelligence is concerned, while female intelligence tends towards a mean, so that the average woman is intellectually more capable than the average man. Psychological tests show that a man's intelligence may reach higher peaks than a woman's, but that it is less capable of prolonged application.

The sex drive of the male is more constant, more easily aroused, more physical, and less controllable. That of the woman, although just as real and acute, is more complex, more involved with other factors such as affection and emotion, and has a spiritual quality that is usually lacking in the male.

Summing up these differences, there are some males who are superior to some females, but the reverse is true just as often. In our society, a man may achieve fame more easily than a woman, but that is probably due to the fact that in our culture the cards are stacked in favor of the man being successful. But man also fails more frequently in life; he has a higher mental deficiency and mental breakdown rate; he commits suicide three or four times more frequently than does the female; and in the matter of vice and crime he outdoes women about eight to one. When it comes to downright folly, man is far weaker than woman.

The final conclusion in any comparison between the sexes must be that neither is really "the weaker sex." There are sex differences in capacities just as there are differences in biological roles. If society had been wisely constructed, instead of haphazardly as it had to be, the two sexes would be entirely and absolutely equal, their varying capacities and talents allowed to dovetail and complement each other for more effective and richer human living.

Without question, when we look at the way society is organized, it is evident that it is stratified with man at the top, and that he has probably taken for himself most of the advantages. But this does not mean that he is innately superior.

Equality between the sexes has still not been attained. There is no question that man has held the upper hand and that woman's status has always been the lower. There have been societies in which the husband had the right of life and death over his wife; others in which he could beat and abuse her at will; and in virtually every society she has been discriminated against politically, economically, socially, and morally.

In spite of the recent trend in Western civilization towards the emancipation of women, it would be a mistake to assume that social equality between the sexes has now been achieved. The lot and status of woman has come far in the last hundred years, but it has still a long way to go. Public opinion still keeps women out of some activities and handicaps her in others.

She is the last to be hired by most employers, and the first to be fired. Her rate of pay is usually less, even though the caliber of her performance is the same as a man's. The laws in many states regarding property rights, place of residence, and the like, still discriminate against women. The Equal Rights Amendment has not been passed by Congress although the measure has been before it for 25 years or more. The Amendment reads:

> "Equality of rights under the law shall not be denied or abridged by the United States or by any state on account of sex."

● Failure is Not Due to Anything in Women as Women

We may be quite certain, therefore, that the conditions that bring women into the doctors' offices with E.I.I. are not a result of any weakness in women, are not due to the old mistaken idea that they are "the weaker sex."

And in talking to thousands of these women I am quite certain that their difficulties are not due to any stress that woman's subordinate position in society places upon her. It is apparent enough that the majority of women bear their social inequality quite easily and do not let it affect them in the least.

● The Failure in Women's Lives Comes Chiefly Out of Marriage

In discussing their problems with thousands of women patients with E.I.I., it is apparent that the great bulk of it issues from marital and family problems. This is true also in the men, although they, more than women, have some of the source of their difficulties outside the home.

There is some evidence, although it is not sufficiently rich to be conclusive, that *single* women have E.I.I. much less frequently than do *married* women. For instance, Dr. Floyd M. Martinson found in a large series of studies that emotional difficulties were markedly less frequent among single than among married women. And in reviewing more than a thousand consecutive cases of E.I.I., I have found that the incidence of single women in the total is only 6 per cent, whereas the best available figures are that single women comprise 18 per cent of all women. In the same series of patients it would appear that bachelor men comprised 36 per cent of all the men patients, and in the male population at large single men comprise only 23 per cent of the total.

The problem that the married women are having boils down to an inability to meet the situations that marriage and raising a family pose for them.

These situations are of a wide variety, although certain patterns keep repeating themselves, and are more in evidence than other patterns. The root of the matter invariably is that the woman has been faced by a situation to which she frequently did not have the answer and for which she finds no ready, easy solution. It is the demand for capacities that she does not have that gradually wears down her powers of adjustment, of flexibility, and reaction. Her failing ability leads to final frustration and dogged defeat. That is the general pattern.

And that is where we find the answer to our question: "What is wrong with women?"

The chief trouble with women is that the job that society and biology has given them—that of managing a marriage and raising a successful family—is the greatest of all possible human achievements and it is the most difficult. It calls for abilities in the abstract, for talents of a most exacting nature, for personal qualities of the highest sort, and for *adequate* training (which she seldom gets) in the art and science of its accomplishment. Adequate training not being available, the element of personal incapacity being great, and the problems in marriage (including of course, the husband component) being so difficult—these are the final reasons why so many women develop E.I.I. in the course of their lives.

● **What Does Woman's Life Hold That Is Good?**

There is no question that woman's life is more drab, less creative, less thrilling, less meaningful, more confining, more

replete with thankless drudgery and trivial irksome irritations,
less rewarding, and generally harder than man's.

In a nationwide poll by "Fortune Magazine," Elmo Roper
found that 25 per cent of all women would prefer to live their
lives over as men if they could, whereas only 3 per cent of men
would prefer to lead their second existence as women.

The average woman's working hours are much longer than
the average man's. She has a seven-day-a-week job, and she
is occupied with it from the moment she arises in the morning
until she goes to bed at night. What is more, housework is the
sort of thing that always gives her a feeling that things are
never done. The bathroom is scrubbed, and before long it
needs to be scrubbed again; every moment there are a dozen
undone tasks that hang over her; the silverware all needs cleaning, there is washing in the basement; the attic closets should
be cleaned; there is always another meal just around the
corner, and the last dishes are waiting to be washed.

But there is another important point to woman's life—a point
even more important than the fact that her life is drab. That is
the point that if a woman has the curiosity and the desire to
increase her intelligence concerning the world around her—
especially the part of the world in which she has the makings
of an expert, the human relations part—if she has imagination
enough to visualize ways in which she can use her talents in
influencing and shaping her part of that world, if she has the
capacity and the control of herself to create and bring into
being the ideas she has visualized, she is *not* going to lead a
drab, uncreative life.

Today, with so many of the old restraints removed from
woman's life, her existence can be as free for creative effort as
can a man's. As a matter of fact, more so. Hers can be the
more interesting and the more worthwhile of the two.

● Woman's Job Is the Creation of Human Values

Her job is a better, more interesting, more influential, more
creative job than any of these. Woman is biologically, socially,
and psychologically fitted to the creation of human things and
human values, the type of values that the race needs more
sorely than any others. Human things and human values are
her specially designed field—values between herself and the
people she meets, between herself and her husband, values

that she creates in her children, in her family, in her community from the neighborhood level to the federal level. Hers is the innate power to increase the value of human capabilities in dealing with other human beings, of enlarging and refining personal and social values that may already exist.

These are not abstract, intangible values. They are very practical and real.

● *A Woman Can and Should Create New Values in the Husband*

She does this, not by domineering, nagging, pushing, or wheedling, but by skillfully understanding him, his capacities, his limitations, enlisting and awakening his interests, building his confidence and abilities, helping him as she would a child to bring out the best qualities he has. The ability of the wife to do this is part of her "ability in the abstract," part of her capacity if she is to be measured a success in her own right and in her own way.

A woman should not marry a man passively to be his mistress, his cook and his housekeeper. She should marry with the idea of being an active partner who is going to make a presentable man out of her husband. Into her marriage it is she who must bring the imagination of creating a wholesome companionship between them. The chances are that, if it is to be done, *she* is the one who will have to do it, who will have the sense to do it, the capacity for doing it; he will most probably not have. Her job at once is to understand *him*, to help him understand himself, to help him rise to *his* capacities, to encourage him, and to give him some of her vision. Many a raw wilderness of a man has been fashioned into something worthwhile by a woman without whom he would have floundered all his life.

As a matter of fact, there isn't a man who doesn't need the right woman to make something out of him. That's her first creative job and one she has as long as they live.

The woman helps "sell" her husband to his associates. As the family expert in personal relations, as the adroit manipulator of things human, she can be a prime factor in raising her husband in the esteem of the people with whom he works. If she does it correctly, manages her associations smartly, she can be a terrific force for increasing the good will of his colleagues toward her husband. This too is included in her "ability in the abstract."

She is the active partner in charge of contacts, human relations, personnel management, personal "fixer de luxe." In all of these roles she can be an indispensible help, or a complete flop if she fails.

But that is only a starter for her creative efforts.

The woman creates new people and creates their values. She gives birth to a new human being—to two, to three, or more. These are entirely new lives over which she has control; what they become is more dependent upon her capacities than upon any other single factor. They will be as good as what she can put into them. She nourishes them, feeds them, cares for them during their most impressionable and formative years. Hers is the power of making them or breaking them, making their whole lives good or making their whole lives miserable and nightmares of maladjustment. What man has such a creative opportunity?

Hers too is the job of making the family either a fine unit of living or a big bust for everyone in it. If she has capacity, hers is the power to create out of the family a unit of mutual affection, mutual joy, mutual cooperativeness, with everyone in it having the family enterprise at heart.

Those are her big immediate opportunities for valuable, interesting, thrilling, creative living. But her rightful field does not stop there.

The woman can and should create community and civic values. Every community, and the world at large, is sadly in need of the human values and humanitarian outlook that women can bring to its problems. It is becoming too apparent that much of human society, at the local as well as the the world level, has been warped by male aggressiveness and selfishness. Woman should make her influence felt more and more and bring to our political and social problems her outlook that our primary concern must be the welfare of human beings— *every human being.*

A woman, every woman and any woman, can be a creative influence for neighborhood projects, for better schools, for better local efforts of all kinds. She can help direct local, state and federal government efforts toward projects which enrich human life rather than the politician's pockets.

By judicious, well-planned housekeeping she can find herself an hour or two every day for writing, for studying, for painting, for weaving, for jewelry making, for piano lessons, for attending lectures, for working for some worthwhile organization. She can plan, create, and keep a home that is a delight to those who live in it.

● *There is Nothing Drab About a Woman's Creative Life*

A woman's life is drab only if *she* is drab. It is uncreative only if she is uncreative, and uninteresting only if she allows herself to remain uninteresting and uninterested. Her limitations are the same limitations that strangle a man's life—limitations of imagination, self-development, vision, and finally, effort. She may decorate a house drably because she never developed the capacity and she never took the effort to gain the know-how for decorating it thrillingly and creatively. Her life can be a constant round of unrewarded drudgery because she hasn't the imagination to invent an outlet that is rewarding, or a project that is a relief from drudgery.

II. WHAT IS WOMAN'S GREATEST NEED?

● *Are There More Discontented Women Than Contented Ones?*

Which are the more numerous, the contented or the discontented women? On the basis of many surveys that all give about the same answer, 63 per cent of the women in this country are happy and content. This percentage is not as high as it should be, or as it can be if attention is paid to the vital factors responsible for the discontent and unhappiness.

● *The American Woman Is Free to Be an Individual*

The statement about women in America having it so wonderful quite rightly infers that she has more freedom to be an *individual*—that is to say, more freedom to live a life of her own design, to wield and exert her influence as an individual, to make the decisions that direct the course of her life and her family's life, to assume responsibility for her own plans. This freedom of action and dignity of individualism belongs to the American woman whether she chooses marriage as a career or whether she enters some business or profession.

Her freedom of action has many different facets, and as examples of these we might mention such important ones as the freedom to choose between marriage and a career in virtually any other field, to choose a husband to her liking, to choose the kind of home she wants, even to choosing outside work to augment the family income in order to get the kind of home she wants, the choice to divorce if her marriage is unhappy.

● Freedom Means Added Responsibility

The thing we must remember, and never forget, in making the statement "How nice the American woman has it today," is that the new freedom is not the kind of freedom implied in having "a high old time" on a week-end holiday. Instead, it is the kind of freedom from top management supervision and someone else's rules that a vice president of a concern achieves when he becomes president. Certainly he has a new freedom; certainly he has never had it so good; and most assuredly— and don't forget this—he has never needed so much ability and capacity before, nor has he ever assumed so much responsibility.

● Why so Many of Today's Women Are Unhappy

These last two provisions are the basis for the fact that so many women are discouraged, complaining and unhappy. They are trying to manage their complicated role of liberated homemaker without adequate ability. It required less ability to be the old-fashioned type of wife who had all her decisions made by her husband and all of her thinking and activity cut out for her by set conventions, than to be the kind of wife who has as much to say about everything, including finances, as the husband, and more to say than the husband about the children, about the kind of home she wants, and about the kind of outside activity she wishes to engage in. Such a new arrangement calls for more ability, *as well as for more work*— the ability for shrewd financing, better cooking, better house-keeping, more creative imagination to maintain the high American standard of living in the matter of houses, meals, clothes, education and recreation—than any other marriage arrangement has ever required before. Who but the American woman, ably abetted by the American advertising salesman, could have raised our standard of living to so high a level?

So we have to face it. Woman's life *is* better; but to take full advantage of it she needs to be a better and more competent woman.

● *The Special Quality That Today's Woman Needs*

It is hard to define, in any concise or brief way, the particular quality that today's woman needs, or to give it a precise name. The name that best fits the sort of thing we are talking about is *maturity.*

"Maturity" is a name for a definite set of qualities and abilities. It is precisely these qualities and abilities that are the missing element whose lack is primarily responsible for the anxiety in people's lives, for the complaining, the restlessness, the unhappiness. Seeing this group of American women, as the physician sees them daily in his office, one is impressed by the fact that nine out of ten of them are under emotional stress because they lack one or more of the essential elements of maturity. One sees in men, too, that their difficulties stem similarly from their immaturities.

These men and women have never entirely grown up! They are trying to deal with their adult problems with the attitudes of children.

● *Meeting the Present Need for Adult Help in Maturing*

In the meantime, in a growing number of doctors' offices, emotionally induced illness is being met in a very basic way by trying to teach what it means to be mature; showing these men and women how they are lacking, where they are lacking, and how mature attitudes and actions can be used to bring order into the now-unsatisfactory areas of their living.

But those who are immature enough to be having trouble in managing their lives should not have to wait until they get to the doctor's office.

Indeed, they do not have to wait. If one knows what maturity *is,* what the elements are that go into its composition, one can acquire a satisfactory amount of it, just as one can gain almost any sort of an education on his own if one has the will to go about it.

If you are such a woman, and feel an incompetence in the way you are meeting your responsibilities, if you are having trouble accomplishing the duties required of you, are perhaps already restive, unhappy, and discouraged, this book is intended to help you.

As you read, we will try to answer the question, "What does

a woman need to lead a successful and happy life in our sort of world?" This question, and the answers given in this book, pertain particularly to the 81 per cent of women who chose marriage as their career. But it is also applicable to the remaining 19 per cent who have chosen a career other than homemaking.

After you read the book through and see what the elements are that make up maturity, you will find in Chapter 15 some idea of how you may go about acquiring some of these various maturities.

● What Maturity Is and How You Benefit by Having It

Maturity is the collection of attitudes that enables one to handle adult situations in a way that is beneficial to oneself and to all the others involved.

Maturity thus defined very clearly means successful living, and successful living, of course, is happy living.

● A Family Example of Immaturity and Maturity

By way of illustrating the definition, let us present an example of the sort of situation any mother might meet.

Billy and his younger sister, Jane, are playing together in the living room, and they get into a dreadful argument over who owns what; it doesn't make any particular difference what, let us say a magnifying glass. They try vainly to pull it out of each other's hand, and Billy finally hits his sister in the face, and sister bursts into high wailing and many tears, more out of an injured sense of justice than from the blow.

Mother rushes in *angrily* and says, "Billy, you are a bad, mean boy! I'll give you a whack, too!" And she gives Billy a good cuffing over the ears. "How do you like that!"

Billy, his dander up, retorts, "And you are a bad, mean Mamma," and he slaps his mother in the face.

Then the mother hits back three times, so hard it hurts, and although there is still belligerency left in Billy, it is no longer being mobilized.

Which one acted more like a child?

It was an immature way for mother to act. It did not benefit her because Billy's estimate of her as a person and as a disciplinarian dropped several notches. Nor is he going to be any better for this method of disciplining. No one benefited; it was not a mature way of meeting the situation.

Suppose now the mother had said, seriously but not unpleasantly, "Now, Billy and Jane, come over here to me. Don't you see, children, you are spoiling all your fun by being selfish. You'll both have much more fun if you let each other have things. And, Billy, in this family people simply do not slap other people. You wouldn't like it if I hit you, would you? So, you, Billy, and you, Jane, each go to your room, close your doors, and when you have decided that the other can play with the glass for a while, you may come out again."

That is much more mature, first, because she didn't act like a child herself, but more importantly, it was mature because it was a problem solution that benefits her because it elevates her in both Jane's and Billy's esteem, and because it teaches Jane and Billy a useful lesson that will benefit them later.

● Maturity Is a Very Practical Thing

You will be surprised to see that maturity is after all a matter of dealing with practical things in a very practical way. There is nothing "high-hattish" about maturity.

You will also be surprised that maturity is composed of a set of factors that are more nearly *attitudes* than anything else, attitudes of a certain kind toward the things that happen to us in life. Maturity in the strict sense is rarely a matter of judgment, unless we mean judgment in forming and adopting mature attitudes. We shall see, as we proceed, that maturity is a matter of the attitudes you bring to the choice of a husband, to living with a husband, to the problem of raising a family, rather than an intellectual acuity in solving crossword puzzles, getting the better of some witty nuisance sitting beside you at a banquet table, or knowing what stocks to buy.

Every one of these attitudes you have heard of before. Some of them you already have and in that sense you are already partially mature. Some of them you do not have, simply because no one ever made you aware that they were necessary, or even that they were possible to attain.

It is the practical sort of thing—this practical sort of attitude filled with know-how—that we mean when we talk of maturity.

For some of the attitudes it is hard to find a suitable name. The thing the psychiatrists and psychologists are talking about may not be *exactly* the same thing implied by terms that have been in popular use. This is true of the term we have used for designating one factor in maturity as "having *consideration* for other people." In its usual meaning, this term does not denote exactly what the psychologist means when he speaks of "being able to *identify* oneself with someone else."

In all such cases we have retained the commonly used word, and call this particular maturity an attitude of *consideration,* rather than an attitude of *identification.*

This policy seems to us to keep the whole matter of maturity on the level at which all of us, who are not psychologists or psychiatrists, live. The terms of maturity need to be understandable to people generally, all of whom equally need maturity. Any particular discussion of maturity must show its application to the common world in which we all live, in which we eat, sleep, love, hate, fight, cooperate, and raise families.

With that general idea in mind we have in this book reduced and catalogued the evidence gathered by psychiatry and psychology into different categories, each separate category being called a "maturity." These are given in Table 1 on page 16.

A TABLE OF THE MATURITIES

Maturities	Page	Immaturities
Attitudes That Are Good For People		**Attitudes That Are Bad For People**
1. Having a predictably pleasant disposition, and a sense of humor.	25 38	Having a moody, sour, crabby disposition.
2. Able to make the most of it, and to rise above adversity.	50 68	Forever nursing a feeling of being abused, of self-pity, of deep dissatisfaction.
3. Being unselfish (or having enlightened selfishness) with Consideration for others, A giving attitude, and Stealing nothing, cheating no one.	84 100 106	Self-centered, selfish, egotistical. Dishonest.
4. Living courageously and confidently.	108	Living in constant fear of vague and unreal dangers.
5. Unaffected by tremendous trifles nor needing to stoop to anger.	122	Easily irritated and upset. Quickly aroused to anger.
6. Having a tenderness for things human.	134	Cruel, mean, hostile and aggressively unpleasant.
7. Liking work and responsibility.	142	Lazy, irresponsible.
8. Mixing common sense with fancy.	160	Accepting fancy or hypothesis as fact.
9. Able to make sex a happy part of life.	190	Making a mess of sex.
10. Having interests beyond oneself.	211	Interested in little beyond one's own small circle.
11. Being self-reliant and able to make decisions.	221	Unable to make decisions. Dependent on others.

What a Woman Needs

To Be Successful and Happy

The distaff Director of the Wyalusing Conferences, on a side channel of the Wisconsin River.

Pulling the canoes ashore for the night's camp.

The last four miles of the Wisconsin with Wyalusing looming downstream, with Pike's Peak in the extreme distance on the Iowa side of the Mississippi.

Wyalusing seen from Pike's Peak on the Iowa side. The Wisconsin curves from the middle distance to its confluence with the Mississippi, which lies 600 feet directly below.

The Wyalusing Family Conferences—

How This Book Began

This book came into being in an unusual and perfectly delightful way. It was written, a bit at a time, over many years, from the discussions between two parents and their three teen-age daughters.

The setting of the discussions was a very colorful one, a setting that so influenced its tone of basic humanitarianism that I have thought it desirable to preserve, as far as possible, the atmosphere in which the substance of this book was formed.

Every year in October, the family of three daughters and their parents paddled two canoes, one red and one silver, down the swift flowing waters of the lower Wisconsin River from Prairie du Sac to Prairie du Chien, a distance, as a car travels, of 110 miles, but considerably farther as the sinuous river flows.

October was chosen for the annual pilgrimage for several reasons.

Wisconsin October is almost uniformly a dream of golden sunshine under a rainless sky of deep, deep blue. The days are mellow, soft, and warm, while the nights are chilly enough to banish flies and mosquitoes, and sharp enough to demand the comfort of a jovially brisk camp fire, an indispensable influence for basic humanitarianism in any discussion between people.

But most important of all, Wisconsin October, from the 10th to the 18th, explodes into a riotous carnival of fall color. The white birch takes on sunbright yellows and golds, the maple turns crimson, Chinese red, and flaming mixtures of saffrons and maroons, the oak changes into surprisingly modulated and endlessly variegated shades of pastel lavenders, purples, and warm rich shades of reds and golds.

The great wooded bluffs that form a double rampart for the river burst into a fortissimo of coloration. It becomes a new world, unlike the old; a world, as one goes down the river, that is a breathtakingly beautiful kaleidoscope of yellows, crimsons, purples, and magentas.

Through it all the river moves with a hardly audible gurgling murmur, in, out, around, and over its sand bars of golden sand.

All that is why October became the month for the annual pilgrimage.

The annual pilgrimage became a tradition in the family as soon as the girls were able to handle a loaded canoe in the river currents and able to swim in the event either of the canoes upset. Except for the father, who was essential in the early days as a stern paddler and tent putter-upper, and in later years, perhaps, as a balancing mind, the excursion was entirely a feminine affair. It was always the girls, girls, girls who had so many grand qualities, so much charm, lightheartedness, idealism, and love of life. It was always the girls, happy and gay, who spiced the talk as a meal cooked over driftwood on a sandbar under a warm noonday sun. It was always the girls who started harmonizing, or laughing over

stories around the campfires at night, campfires the
family will always remember for the great horned
owl's repeated whoo-whoooo-whoo-whooooooo, for
the nighthawk's rough laconic note and for the whip-
poorwill's staccato somewhere out in the black night
air.

It was the oldest daughter who quietly raised the
question (as the family was thoughtfully watching the
light and shadow of a night campfire) that became
the accepted theme of discussion on the Wisconsin
River journeys and which has become the theme of the
book. The daughter was concerned with the intricate
matters that are involved in raising a successful family.

The conversation had drifted into the general subject of the three girls' futures, and after some general
discursive banter, the oldest daughter remarked:

"It all seems sort of ridiculous. Girls are sent to college to prepare for a career and to make their own
living; then shortly after we graduate we marry and
have a family. We learn very little about that, but I
am certain it is much more difficult than being a
teacher, or a secretary, or a lawyer. I, for one, feel
terrified by what I don't know about raising a family
properly and managing a husband. And yet I feel
certain that eventually that is the career I'm going in
to, because I think it is the most wonderful career a
woman can have."

Right then and there, the five members of the family
decided that each annual October Pilgrimage was to
be given over to a discussion of some part of that
theme: *How Can A Woman Best Manage Her Life?*

And so it began.

The discussions were always lively, whether gay or
serious. The talk rippled from canoe to canoe as they
skimmed over the thoughtful river. The discussion

would start bubbling with the coffee pot at breakfast as the cool morning mist curled over the camp, and it would leap with the flames around the night camp-fires.

Whatever was said along the four-day course down the river was finally culled down, organized and sum-marized on the fifth and last day and night, in a camp held fittingly on Olympian Wyalusing, the grandest bluff on all the river, overlooking the confluence of the Wisconsin and the Mississippi. Here, in the great outdoor night under the billions of stars of a great universe, looking down into the mysterious night-shrouded depths of two great river valleys, sur-rounded by the calls and sounds of the forest, oc-curred what the family came to refer to, half seriously and half jokingly, as the "Wyalusing Conferences."

During the ensuing year the five family members each thought over what had been said, and each planned something to say on the next pilgrimage and at the next conference.

The content of this book is the substance of these "Wyalusing Conferences"—necessarily edited, re-vised, and regrouped, but unchanged in its essentials.

Feeding these discussions were the keenly directed questions of the girls, asked out of the mixture of their hopes and fears, their wonderings and their dreams. The answers were as good as the inspiration of the time and the place, and as the abilities of the five would allow, and were admittedly as tentative as the whole of human life. But at any rate they were answers, by people striving to give honest answers to the problems that plague and pursue any woman who takes on a marital partner—good, bad, or indif-ferent, for better or for worse—and rears a family. The answers were based quite largely on the experiences

of the mother, who had earlier been a college professor, and on the experiences of the father, who was
a practicing physician. But the girls added much to
the answers, too, with insights gained in school and
in family living.

In the long run, I suppose the girls contributed as
much to the discussion as the parents, especially in
items that affected the atmosphere of the discussions,
such as the sympathetic observation one of them made
that although the world is so wonderful that all of us
ought to be glad to be alive, there is always the sad-
ness in the world that people, beginning with high
hopes and dreams, end so often with a life that has
all the disappointment and character of a wet, soggy,
mildewed loaf of bread.

It was quite generally agreed that women's faces,
after they were 50, showed the wear and tear of a
discouraging life more often than did the faces of
men, and that the way our society is constructed
places a handicap on being a woman. The girl standing tiptoe looking into womanhood is usually more
idealistic, also more realistic, much more imaginative,
much more sensitive than the boy looking into manhood. The world the girl enters is more difficult than
the one the boy enters. At the end the relative descent
of her high hopes is the greater because she started
higher and ended lower. During her life, the girl is
apt to find that her sensitiveness, her fine longings and
hopes, are only disadvantages in the kind of world
in which she finally finds herself.

After considerable discussion, we five who journeyed
yearly to the Wyalusing Conference, came to the
general agreement that building the family is primarily the woman's task, and that so many families
are failures because so many women are failures.

They are failures because no one really showed them how to be anything other than that. We also agreed that when it is done well, building a fine family is just about the most admirable accomplishment of man, and requires probably more ability than does any other enterprise.

Perhaps one should not be so harsh as to call any group of mothers failures. Perhaps just bringing a set of children into the world and then grimly hanging on through crisis after crisis, argument after argument, woe after woe, trouble after trouble, through heavy worries and thin finances, perhaps this alone should be classed as a sort of success. God knows it entails hardship enough—and a battlefield type of hardship at that—to merit the mother a decoration from the President of the United States. But with due respect to the element of achievement that her family does contain, nevertheless she and her family are still failures. The children are reared under conditions that insure the same kind of failure in them. The poor woman's life, in spite of its heroic resistance to all the horrors of hell on earth, is far from the success she naively anticipated at sixteen.

And so, on the river journeys and on Wyalusing, the five of us tried to give answers to two questions:

- **Why do so many women fail in making a success of marriage and in building a good family?**
- **How is a woman possibly to avoid this failure?**

1

A Predictably Pleasant Disposition
and How to Acquire It

Maturity No. 1

The easiest way to be miserable is to have a lousy disposition. It is also the simplest and most direct way to make the people you live with miserable.

Similarly, the easiest way to turn your life into a reasonably happy experience is to cultivate a cheerful, pleasant disposition.

Your disposition is the most important single factor for living enjoyably, regardless of whether you are rich or poor, smiled or frowned upon by fortune.

A mellow disposition is hardly ever found without a considerable degree of maturity of other varieties. But cultivating a pleasant disposition is an excellent place to begin maturing. A pleasant disposition, practically unassisted by other maturities, will make disagreeable circumstances bearable and insignificant. Nor is there any other quality that will bring you the friendship of others so readily.

But the most important reason for placing a good disposition first on our list of maturities is that having a pleasant disposition makes it easier to acquire the other maturities. A person with a good disposition learns more easily and is much more receptive to the other maturities than is a nasty, sour-dispositioned person.

Any person with a nasty disposition will scoff at what we have said so far in this chapter, and will be in a disagreeable, mean, frame of mind. There is nothing a person feels he must defend as strongly as the weakness of his childish disposition. But we urge him to come along. Once he sees the need, he too can improve his disposition. The obvious fact will trickle into his mind that the most perfect circumstance imaginable becomes valueless the instant a sour, moody disposition takes it over.

No human being really deserves the misery that an unpleasant disposition brings him. But much more pitiful and much less deserved is the misery a person innocently suffers by having to live with such a sour pickle.

● Is Disposition Really a Matter of Maturity?

At first sight some may wonder whether *disposition* really belongs in the category of being a maturity or an immaturity. But most assuredly it does, as a moment's reflection will show. There are two features that put any quality into the category of being an immaturity or maturity, and the quality we call "disposition" clearly has them both.

First of all, your disposition is entirely a quality you are conditioned to; it is something you must learn. You have the disposition you were taught to have.

Secondly, a poor disposition will bring you, and those unfortunate enough to have to live with you, a great amount of trouble, but a good disposition will benefit you and everyone else.

Those are the two distinguishing and definitive earmarks that label a maturity.

● What Kind of Disposition Is "Normal" and Desirable?

Many people are of the opinion that the kind of disposition one has is as natural and unavoidable as the kind of nose one has, and that one type of disposition is no more normal or natural than any other.

We have all gravitated and settled into our customary disposition so easily that it appears to us as the only disposition any human being can properly have.

The most important conditioning factor that determines the disposition we acquire is the disposition of people in our family in childhood. Dispositions are handed down from generation to generation, and the disposition that prevails in a family was probably the disposition the 300th-removed ancestor had as a cave-dweller. People of similar disposition tend to marry. There is nothing, not even an unconscious facial resemblance, that attracts *like* and *like* and leads to marriage as often as does a similarity in disposition.

• Children's Dispositions Are Unpredictable and Often Disagreeable

The disposition of the average child is like mountain weather, variable and unpredictable. One moment the sun shines warmly, the next a storm pops over the summit and fills the air with black clouds and hail.

It is precisely this unpredictable and often disagreeable disposition of the child that frazzles the nerves of a mother. Instead of being the bright bundle of happiness that children are often pictured to be, they very frequently are disagreeable, irritable, nasty, and wholly unpredictable in mood. The average childhood is not a very happy one, despite the absence of the demands and responsibilities which cause stress in adult life.

Most people grow out of their childhood *fears* rather well, but a great many people do not mature very far out of their childhood *disposition*. This is because they get so very little help in the matter. The chances are the parents never matured very far beyond their own childhood dispositions, nor did their parents before them.

There are outside influences, though, that can deflect a child's disposition from the family pattern—a neighbor, a friend, an uncle or an aunt, or anyone who happens to have a forceful personality.

Other things being equal, a colicky baby will start developing a colicky disposition, while a baby with a healthy, robust digestive system will tend to have a healthy, robust disposition and be responsive to the influence of his parents in a favorable way.

So "normally" and "naturally" we have the dispositions we were conditioned to have in childhood.

● Is the Individual with a Steady, Good Disposition Uninspiring and Insipid?

Here again the objection is beside the point. A person can be uninspiring and insipid, or forceful and inspiring, regardless of whether he has a disposition of one extreme or the other.

Being inspiring or uninspiring is largely a matter of qualities other than disposition.

Some people of high and inspiring capacity, like H. L. Mencken, George Bernard Shaw, and Jean Jacques Rousseau, did have cutting and sarcastic dispositions. But others of even higher capacity, like William Shakespeare, Albert Einstein, Albert Schweitzer, Isaac Newton, Bertrand Russell, Benjamin Franklin, just to name a few, possessed wonderful dispositions.

As for the disposition itself, which is the more inspiring, an habitually unpleasant or an habitually pleasant one?

Is there anything inspiring, either to oneself or to others, in blowing one's top and frequently acting in a childish, critical jumpy fashion? No one finds much value in having to live with someone who keeps pawing up the ground like an enraged bull. Have *you* ever had to live, for even a few hours, with someone who has a volcanic disposition, or a thorn-thicket disposition, or a "dirty-kitchen" disposition? How inspired did you become? How enjoyable was such a life? There is immeasurably more beauty and good in a sunrise or sunset than in a violent storm.

The person who is rude, sullen and sarcastic is precisely the one who argues that such a disposition is to be preferred to a kindly, gentle, and pleasant one.

In America the idea that an irascible disposition is the desirable one was promulgated in this century by a very able writer (no longer alive) who had a keen and ready intelligence. But he had the disposition of a 30-degree-below-zero morning —inhuman, cutting and uncomfortable.

His guillotine mind found its pleasure in letting heads fall willy-nilly. His pleasantries had the touch of concentrated hydrochloric acid. The older he got the more things and people he disliked, and the more vitriolic he became, until literally he could hardly live with himself. He was as miserable inside as he was nasty outside. He was forever suffering from a disabling illness which he himself termed "sinus trouble" and "bad digestion," two maladies for which a long list of eminent medical consultants could give him no relief, an almost certain sign that an illness is emotionally induced. So many of his type of self-driving small geniuses are chronically ill with what is at bottom an emotionally induced illness. He was a bellowing bull on the contemporary scene, but the chances are he will be appropriately forgotten by the next generation.

● **The Impulsive, Assertive Disposition Is a Sad and Juvenile Error**

There is another objection raised to a pleasant disposition that is based on an opinion made popular in our time, and which has not yet been laid to rest in the cold coffin where it belongs.

A number of psychologists and psychiatrists advocate that people should behave in what they term an "uninhibited" way. They believe that inhibitions imposed by society or oneself produce inner conflicts, and it is these conflicts that make people unhappy, anxious, and tense. They insist that a person must remain juvenile in expressing, saying and doing the things he wishes to do. If you are *impelled* to tell your boss he is an unbearable fool and a stuffed shirt, you must tell him so, and not suffer with a repressed impulse. This may leave you without a job and but two dollars in your pocket. But no matter, they say, you are really lucky not to be successful in the conventional way since being successful depends so largely on repressing impulses. Revel in the fact you are rid of your impulses. Be glad you are not the executive type, all of whom are horribly inhibited, are beyond help in fact. If you are given the opportunity of expressing your opinion of the hostess' dinner, have no inhibitions—tell her what a miserable flop it was. Or if you disagree with a speaker—talk up, or stalk out loudly, or both, to show your disapproval. Giving expression to impulses may not make you popular, but it should make you happy.

The entire idea is as tragically wrong as are its consequences.

Just where you are to stop in this matter of being uninhibited is never definitely stated but is left dangling like a noose inviting your head. Perhaps you are to stop just short of breaking the law; or perhaps the police had better be disposed of so that everyone may be less inhibited.

Somewhere along the line you are obviously going to have to curb your impulses or you begin to make more trouble for yourself than you avoid by being uninhibited. Where is that dividing line? They never say. Apparently you are to figure that one out for yourself—it's a good mental exercise! Which side of the line does it fall on to tell everyone off whom you don't like, quite candidly, including your boss? Should a man remove the inhibition to kiss every pretty girl he sees? Should one inhibit a strong impulse to set fire to a building?

The wholly "uninhibited" person could not be allowed to exist as a free agent in society any more than a child can be allowed absolutely free reign. Even the uninhibited person who stays on the safe side of the police will make more trouble for himself in the long run than the experiment is worth.

We all have to learn to live with others or else be removed from society by being sent to jail or be isolated in some other way. We also must learn to live with ourselves, inside ourselves.

● *What Are Impulses?*

Some ways of meeting problems are better than others. It has been a basic experience of the human race that resorting to what is called "impulse" is usually an ineffective way of meeting a situation.

The simple truth of the matter is that the "impulses" we feel, these "natural" juvenile urges, are not "natural," basic qualities at all. They are impulses which themselves have been conditioned; they, too, are attitudes that we once learned. They are basic only in the sense that they are very primitive and elementary conditioning, they are half-baked learnings, and like anything half-baked, they are a disadvantage.

The juvenile tendency to say what one thinks is conditioned by a belief in one's unequivocable rightness, one of the earliest and subtlest egotistical conditionings we acquire. The man who tells his boss off is already conditioned to feel satisfaction at putting that big phony in his place. Unfortunately the same childish conditioning doesn't make him satisfied with finding himself out of a job and out of an income. Those who advocate living according to such "impulses" consider their own impulses "natural" and unconditioned, and interpret their inability to decondition themselves as a "conflict."

A conflict arises when a person's conditioning has been so faulty that he finds himself making his own troubles in adult life. The real conflict is between the poor habits he has learned for meeting situations and the obvious need for learning better methods. A person who has not learned maturity is miserably caught between a situation and his own ineptness in dealing with it. He is indeed the victim of a conflict.

The happily dispositioned person has been conditioned away from outlooks on life that involve outbursts of temper, that resort to nastiness and meanness, that indulge in pouty, sullen moods.

The pleasantly dispositioned person has learned (and been conditioned to) a philosophy of life that makes for equanimity in the face of trouble, a sense of humor that sees the funny or wry element inherent in almost every situation, and the courage to sail a floundering situation into quieter waters.

A happy disposition is not a matter of being either inhibited or uninhibited. It is a matter of attaining insight and vision enough to see that choleric attitudes, anger, meanness, low moods, and anxiety add nothing to any moment except more unnecessary troubles. Many a day may have its difficulties, but none is so bad that a cheerful disposition can't make *something* of it, and no day is so good that a rotten disposition can't ruin it completely and turn it into a day that wasn't even worth getting up for.

● One of Women's Main Troubles Is the Disposition of Men

Men have disagreeable dispositions more commonly than do women. Our culture has always presented the violent disposition as being "masculine," whereas agreeableness and sweetness have always been considered a part of femininity.

The doctor today finds that one of the most common immaturities giving men emotionally induced illness is an unpleasant disposition. He also finds that the most common single stress a woman experiences in marriage is having a husband with such a childish and volatile disposition.

A wife who herself possesses an excellent disposition, can hope to make some improvement in a man who is as sullen and hard to live with as a brickbat. But she may be sure it will require a tremendous amount of patience and effort. It is far, far easier to pick out a good husband in the first place. If unfortunately you were not successful in your choice, you are stuck and have to do as well as you can with the husband you picked.

Only one thin ray of satisfaction pierces the trap that the woman with an immature husband is in, and this her hurt feelings usually do not allow her to see. It is the feeble and sadistic feeling of compensation she gets from realizing that the fellow on the inside of the crabby disposition is even worse off than he appears from the outside.

But this realization is pitifully small compensation for the wife who does a truly creditable day's work in the home with the children, and has managed somehow in the whirl to set a good meal on the table to welcome her husband's homecoming. She is hoping against hope that he may come home with just a little show of affection or a tiny feeling of appreciation, *or even be gay and cheerful for a change.* He comes in instead with an aggressive and derogatory manner that makes her feel like the lowest leper in India.

A husband with a disagreeable disposition gives his wife the same sort of thrill she gets from four baskets of wet wash waiting many days in the basement for the rain to stop.

● *Picking a Husband with a Pleasant Disposition*

It is very difficult to predict what a man's disposition is going to be like after he is married. In his courting days and in his social contacts he is careful not to show his natural disposition. The one he shows is well-groomed and patched up for the occasion so that she will think well of him.

Two premarital clues for picking a husband with a good disposition, or for determining the way the chips are going to fall when he comes to working out his marital relations, are these:

First, on a date, if he has even *short moments* that are irritable and sullen — pull out! He is showing his hand, and you may be sure he has a fist FULL of the same kind of cards. Don't play with *HIM*, or your days will turn into intense regret and futile romance. Go while the going is good.

Second, watch him at a distance when he is with other people and doesn't know you are around. If he is often serious, moody and dull, looking always like threatening rain, or if he readily vents his spleen, and crabs and pouts like a child, escape at once, and for all time, or his nasty tentacles will crush and suffocate you once you are caught. Go! FLEE! Leave the man to some other, less discerning, woman. As a husband, he will grow immeasurably more sullen, moody, and dull than you see him. He will be immeasurably worse in your living room than you saw him in the social world. In the social world he must maintain at least some air of decency and consideration. In his own home, his shoes come off, his feet go up on the table, his hair comes down, his real nature comes out like a grizzly coming out of his cave.

It is at home that he will show himself for what he really is. There he will let the chips fall where they may, which is always on his poor wife, whom he regards as clay under his feet. Having to live with such a man gradually becomes more and more a stifling and unbearable experience. Life has no greater sting than this. Women married to such men are among the most unhappy people on earth—and there are millions of them in these United States because men with unpredictable, unsympathetic, childish dispositions are common.

If ever you are fortunate enough to stumble on a possible husband who is always sunny, pleasant, and cheerful, grab him, gather him up, and run with him to the altar. He will be a joy to live with forever. The chances of being a good provider are in the pleasant-dispositioned man's favor. And you may be sure that half of what he does earn will be yours without an argument. Take him! Get him! Before some vixen gets him and makes *him* miserable.

One word of caution. Don't be deluded into thinking that "the life of the party" is the man with the pleasant disposition you are looking for. In his private life this cut-up is quite likely to be a lemon of a different variety, very apt to be taciturn and hard to live with. The life of the party is frequently a person with wide swings of mood. He looks interesting and happy enough at a party, but he may not be that way at home. Unfortunately, you can't keep him at a party all the time.

● *Women's Troubles with Their Own Dispositions*

It's not fair to needle only the men in this matter of disposition, because there are plenty of women who can stand improvement, and the nastiest disposition in the family can, of course, be on the distaff side. Perhaps there are men so bad they deserve being married to the type of woman variously called a shrew, a Calamity Jane, a sad sack, or a she-devil. But it is an awful, an ultimate, sentence.

Such a woman makes a home from which the husband would strongly prefer to stay away. And stay away as much as possible he does, sooner or later, legally or illegally. Going home to such a shrew has all the attraction of going into a cave hiding a nine-ring rattler. And when a half dozen children have also taken on her disposition, the place really becomes a den of vipers to which the husband, or visitor, (the two may be combined in the husband) comes with a shudder and with extreme reluctance. Such a home is not a place where one can find a lift when a lift is needed.

● A Good Disposition Is Based on a Philosophy

In the final analysis, a good disposition is based on a certain philosophy of life, which the person may hold without ever consciously expressing it. In its essence, the philosophy of a person with a good disposition runs something like this:

It is a good feeling just to be alive.

One has only to stay in tune to find something in almost every moment so harmonious and enjoyable that it sends a warm, silken feeling all the way to one's bones.

Like Walt Whitman, anyone can learn to thrill to everything in the world, to the miracle of a leaf, to the amazingly controlled future that resides in a seed, to the wonderful potential for all manner of things in children, to the colors and shapes and patterns in the landscape and the town, to the human ingenuity of a fine machine or the delicate sensitivity of a poem, to the way our marvelous hands pick up a pen and write, to all the thousands upon thousands of delightful wonders that surround us constantly on every side.

Like Emerson, we can find delight and amazement in the fantastic accomplishments and abilities of people, even the simplest of people. At the same time we find it a delight in bringing a better moment to someone else.

The little routine difficulties in our everyday life are really such trifling affairs they are not worth becoming upset, or nasty about.

The bigger difficulties that fate twists into our lives are best met stoically, with an attempt to illuminate the dark moment by being at least courageous and maintaining our equanimity, and by keeping, if at all possible, a sense of kind humor toward oneself and others.

Certainly people can be troublesome and disagreeable. Certainly people have foibles. But much better than being equally troublesome, equally disagreeable, one had best counter such dispositions in other people with a warmth and forgiveness based on a sympathetic understanding of human beings.

Just playing the game, and serving the human enterprise in some helpful role gives one a pardonable pride and a rich feeling of satisfaction.

In short, there is a very pleasant feeling in feeling pleasantly disposed.

● The Importance to a Woman of a Good Disposition

The best guarantee of a happy marriage, even better than high intelligence, is an habitually pleasant disposition in both man and wife. It would take an unusual lack of some other kind, and an unusual effort in the wrong direction, to make such a marriage go wrong.

There is hardly any maturity a woman has greater need of in living with a husband and bringing up children than a mellow, mature disposition.

If a woman doesn't have it, she can acquire it, once she realizes she needs improvement.

Thoreau remarked, "I know of no more encouraging fact than the unquestioned ability of man to elevate his life by conscious endeavor. It is something to be able to paint a particular picture, or to carve a statue, and so to make a few objects beautiful; but it is far more glorious to carve and paint the very atmosphere and medium through which we look, which morally we can do."

Dispositions can be knowingly improved by staying alert to the state of your disposition, and heading off any mean impulse you may see slipping into the picture. Send it scurrying off before it has a chance to ruin your day and everyone else's.

A woman can become a constant joy to herself, to her children, to her husband, to the world, by being glad she is alive and by showing it; by knowing enough to let tremendous trifles remain trifles, by turning the adversity of defeat into a victory of equanimity and calm acceptance, by lifting each moment from the level of the dull and the ordinary to heights which give them meaning and interest, and by keeping a song in her heart when lesser people are moaning with self-pity.

Such a woman is one of those magnificent people for whom everyone is glad, because the corner of the world she occupies becomes a mighty pleasant estate.

Such women are not impossible. They exist. They are the finest and the most valuable of all people, and every woman can fashion herself in their image.

2

A Sense of Humor Adds
Spice to Life

More About Maturity No. 1

● *A Sense of Humor and a Pleasant Disposition Go Together*

A sense of humor is the inevitable and delightful spouse of a pleasant disposition. The two exist hand in hand; a sense of humor is usually conditioned along with a pleasant disposition.

In a housewife's life, with its variety of dull and serious situations, a sense of humor is a necessity if living is to rise above sordid drudgery. A woman's life will be a sorry thing if she lacks a sense of humor and a pleasant disposition.

That a sense of humor benefits its possessor almost constantly and invariably is a statement admitting very few exceptions. One might, of course, barge into a situation where a sense of humor would be about as beneficial as sitting on a tack. Such might be the case if, in an exuberant mood, some joking remark of yours gets a little out of hand in dealing with someone who has no sense of humor. One must guard, of course, against such regrettable incidents. But if this sort of thing should happen to you inadvertently, you might just as well dismiss it with an inward, secret touch of humor—by telling yourself that the injured and irate person would have been irate and injured anyway by something else, at about the same time. People without a sense of humor are constantly irate over nothing.

I think it can be said that a person with an unpleasant disposition has very little or no sense of humor. There are possibly exceptions to this rule, but personally I have never known an *unpleasant* person with a sense of humor who was worth a nickel. It is naturally possible that Mother Nature, in one of her misshapen jokes, might conjure up the unsavory combination of a person with a sour and malicious disposition who at the same time gives off an air of delicate and tender thoughts that rises about him like Moustache Perfume. Perhaps somewhere in Shakespeare there *is* a character like that.

● **The Distinction Between Wit and Humor**

However, the chances are that such an incongruous individual would have *wit* rather than *humor*. Wit and humor are an excursion up the same road, but on two altogether different parts of it and in very different types of countries.

Wit is the humorous sally of a cunning and sharp mind. Wit generally carries at least a little acid that nips or bites some other mortal, usually one who has his back turned. Wit is quick and sharp like a dagger.

Humor, on the other hand, is something altogether different. It is the dancing of a happy stream down a wooded mountainside, laughing around boulders, giggling gleefully in a downward bounce, bubbling all the while; it is cool, refreshing, and soothing to the head, throat, and feet.

Sigmund Freud, probing analytically into mankind, could understand Continental wit but he could never understand English humor.

A witty person can get to be something of a trial if he is underfoot and overhead all the time. Having him around can be distressingly like carrying a plate that is too hot to hold. Very often such a person is only too well aware that he is a wit. He then whirls and shoots in a constant display of pinwheels and skyrockets, and really becomes a trial by fire when he lets himself get out of hand; his Roman candles shoot all over the place, completely out of control.

The most suitable trysting place for the wit is the smoke-filled atmosphere of the cocktail party. There the dagger thrusts only half-pierce the din being made by the alcoholic chatter of the guests, and sometimes, if the party is not too far gone, wit serves to restimulate the flow of consciousness long enough to allow the guests to imbibe another drink. Other suitable locales for displaying wit exist, but the cocktail party is the safest. Fortunately, through the wisdom of Nature, it is precisely around the cocktail shaker that the wits are most apt to gather.

● Picking the Right Kind of Sense of Humor

You may possibly be one of the many people who do not quite understand what a sense of humor really is. The thing we Americans call *humor* seems to consist of laughing uproariously at our own jokes, and somewhat less loudly at some one else's. Laughter is definitely involved, and unless there is laughter there is no humor.

But a true sense of humor is something more subtle than that. It does not require laughter, though laughter is permissible. Usually it comes on a level below that of an outright laugh. It is a twinkle in the eye; very often it is merely a smile in the making, one you feel rather than show.

It is a constant joy and amusement at just being alive.

A true sense of humor is a delight and amusement with anything and everything in life.

I want to describe English humour for you because this is the variety you must try to understand.

● Discovering a Sense of "Humor"

Because of my own American conditioning to the idea that humor consists of a joke and laughter, I had some little trouble before I acquired the real trick of a sense of humor.

I once picked up an Englishman's book entitled *Sense of Humour* that carried the assurance on its paper jacket that it was "the best of British humour." With delightful expectancy, I carried the book to an easy chair to enjoy it through the long winter's night.[1]

---

[1] Stephen Potter, *Sense of Humour*, New York: Henry Holt & Company, 1954.

I turned the pages of the book with increasing gravity, first one page at a time, then two and three, till shortly I put the book aside altogether. It wasn't funny! What on earth did the man mean by "humour"?

Two years later, after I had mellowed a bit and my sharp edges had been rounded slightly by the buffeting of the years, I chanced to glance at the title of that book again as it lay on the shelf where it had rested all this time, its humor undisturbed.

"It can't be, it simply can't be," I told myself, "that this book, with its title and its assurance on the jacket, doesn't contain even a smile." Incredulous that I could have made such a sorry error, I dragged the book out once more (this time by the hair, determined to wring *something* out of it) and took it to an easy chair, not at all sure of the long winter's night. I started to read with my index finger inserted 20 pages beyond, prepared to shut the book if necessary.

At the end of the first sentence I *sensed* the flicker of a smile on my lips, and a faint pleasurable relaxation of the muscles about my eyes. That was the full extent of my physical reaction. The author, being English, never intended that I strain myself any more than that. And he kept me like that all through the book. From what proved to be a *short* winter's night, I followed him from then through life. I soon learned to click my heels like his, suddenly sidling with a Danny Kaye step-to-one-side, holding and swinging my cane nattily in both hands with the step, then twirling it with one hand in the air as the English author and I hum-de-diddled down the avenue, not actually tickling the ladies under the chin we met, but imagining that we did, which was (diddle-dum-dum-diddle) quite as much fun, and without prolonged and boring consequences. We did not have the slightest intention of being bored, nor even a slight inclination to be detained very long by any one thing in such an interesting world, at a time when everything and everyone, especially everyone, fairly dripped with gay motifs and quaint oddities. On the way we stepped into a pub —as the author said—"partly to have a drink and partly to refresh ourselves with the character of the landlord."

There wasn't a single guffaw in the book. No smile, of course, except the *sense* of one on the lips and around the eyes. Something less than facetious. Very bright with subtlety and keen with phrases that danced with us down the street. It was kindly delight and amusement with life.

In American humor there must be laughter or we feel the humorist has failed. In the best kind of English *humour* there is no laughter; if there is, the humorist has not achieved what he had hoped to achieve.

● *A General, Over-all Sense of Humor*

It is a great advantage to possess both kinds of humor—the American and the English. The American type, with its guffaw, seizes the possible dreariness that creeps into human existence and turns it into a momentary carnival of fun. It's good to laugh. It brings in the sun and assists the candles that have burned too low. However, you can't be constantly humorous in the American sense. There comes a time when you have to stop laughing because of pain in the ribs and muscles. You have to stop joking sometime or you become a jester, a buffoon, a clown, and are labelled as such. Nevertheless, an American sense of humor is a wonderful thing to have; it's like being able to turn on an electric stove anytime and cooking yourself a little jollity. American humor is a ready and always available way to have some fun.

The English type of *humour* includes a number of qualities— gaiety, lightheartedness, kindliness, quick perception of little values in little things—but most of all it is an attitude toward life. That is why you can wear English *humour* all the time; it is a point of view, an attitude toward life in the mature sense. It is almost exactly the attitude we mean most when we refer to "the maturity of a sense of humor and a pleasant disposition."

This sense of humor is a very real *sense* in two ways:

First, it is equally a sense like the sense of taste, sight or touch. It is a perceptive apparatus, awake whenever we are awake, for detecting the little pieces of worth, the grains of gold, the happy little twists and quirks, that reside in everything. Nothing is exempt from this perceptive sense; everything possesses an element of warmth, of interesting values. This perceptive sense stays with you from morning to night, day in and day out, nosing out the grains of gold, and the little meaningful values that reside in those minutiae of life which appear trifles, often boring or dismaying trifles. This sense that gives meaning to trifles is not only a part of the maturity of a pleasant disposition, which we discussed in the previous chapter, but it is similarly a part of the maturity of rising above tremendous trifles, to be considered in Chapter 3. It is, you see, a saving grace.

But this sort of a sense of humor is also a sense in another meaning; it is *good sense.* It is the good sense of wisdom and understanding that consists in finding a usefulness for things we hadn't noticed, and appreciating the worth of people, little people, let us say, and things, little things, we had passed by as insignificant. It is a high sincerity, even more than it is a high gaiety or agreeable lightheartedness. It is, of course, a great humanism. Instead of merely living off the land, it puts something back into it too.

This sort of humor is one of the human race's finest traits, and exists, and always has existed, wherever human beings make the best of their conditions. There are peoples who have developed it probably even further than the English have. In the Swiss Canton of Glarus, for instance, this perception of the quaint and the gay, nestling even in the most unbearably dark nooks of existence, has been introduced into the very speech of the Canton. The speech displays not only a tone of voice, but a syntax, indigenous words heard nowhere else, that send a ripple of amusement through the weary mind, and serves to make bearable a hard existence in the least arable land of Switzerland.

● *It's Never Too Late to Acquire a Sense of Humor*

Even the least likely candidate can acquire a sense of humor if he has some guidance in going about it.

Mrs. Dawson beautifully illustrates the point that hope need never be dead. Hers is a success story in acquiring a sense of humor that should encourage anyone determined to duplicate it.

There were a number of good reasons why Mrs. Dawson was moving rapidly toward a grass widowhood, but the most important was her exceedingly sour disposition. Her husband, Mr. Dawson, was itching to lose sight of her melancholy face and to get out from under the deep shadow of her personality, which lay over the household like a heavily overcast, leaden sky.

Mrs. Dawson was really a smart and capable woman, but the conditioning of her childhood family had imbued her with a sense of seriousness that was painful not only to Dawson, but to herself. Her life had bogged down in the glum mire of worry and serious concern. If she had ever smiled in her life, the occasion had long since been forgotten.

One fine spring morning Mr. Dawson fled the funereal atmosphere of his home for parts unknown (but presumably more joyous), leaving his wife the possession of the family grocery store. It seemed a generous enough contribution toward her support, but one which Dawson considered well worth the losing, especially since its operation would at last give Mrs. Dawson something real to be concerned and worried about.

And indeed, the management of the grocery became Mrs. Dawson's nemesis, as her husband had intended it should.

It was at about this time that her family physician persuaded Mrs. Dawson, and himself also, that only a brighter disposition and a modicum of humor could ever turn the grocery into an asset, could ever bring Mr. Dawson back, or relieve Mrs. Dawson of her headaches. The possibility of such a transformation appeared microscopic indeed, but the situation was something worse than desperate and called for more than desperate measures.

The attempt to bring humor and sweetness to Mrs. Dawson was a last-ditch stand, with Mrs. Dawson mired in the ditch, her doctor beside her equally mired, both engaged in a heroic last effort to turn away the enemy.

The campaign was carefully planned and swiftly put into action.

The first piece of strategy was that Mrs. Dawson should recount a humorous story every day to everyone she met and to every customer who entered the store. Each day she was to have a new story.

Since she hadn't the slightest ability to distinguish a good tale from a poor one, and no sense of appropriateness, the physician and his nurse carefully chose and copied for her use seven stories every week.

It was a new departure for which she had no past experience, for which she had not the slightest aptitude, and about which she was very pessimistic. But she undertook the experiment. She memorized each story word for word—commas, periods, exclamation marks included. At first the way she told them was more humorous than the story itself. But tell them she did, to every customer's infinite amusement. People began to look forward to visits to her store merely to hear Mrs. Dawson's story of the day.

She stuck stubbornly and doggedly to the program, encouraged and coached during her weekly visits to the doctor. Her stock of stories grew; repeating each story so often fixed them permanently in her mind. Gradually she grew more and more adept in her telling, until she could actually ride the punch line down the homestretch like a master.

Then the miracle happened. She began to smile not only at her own stories but at the stories her hearers usually told in return. These she wrote down, memorized, and added to her growing repertoire.

It was a most serious attempt at developing a sense of humor. Slowly it began to work.

The second piece of strategy, introduced when the first was beginning to work, was to have Mrs. Dawson introduce into as many of her private moments as possible, a feeling of gentle and amused delight.

The doctor selected six moments in her day when she was to make an amusing remark to herself. She was given a list of a few sample remarks that would fit each of the six moments, but she was to invent remarks of her own, writing them down afterward and showing them to the doctor as evidence of her progress.

The execution of this phase was more difficult than the first. But Mrs. Dawson clomped into it like a warhorse doing battle.

The first moment chosen for a gentle sally of humor was on arising in the morning. The moment she was out of bed she was to take her mop of hair and her woebegone face before the mirror and say something amusing. After a few attempts she found herself capable of, "It ain't amusing, Doc," or "Great glory what a picture—it would scare a ghost", or "No wonder Dawson ran away. I'd run too if I could get away from it."

The second moment was after she had fixed herself up as prettily as she could for the day. Then she was to address another humorous remark to her mirror. She invented, "Still a frightful appeal in the old gal," "Dawson is sure missing a fine picture this morning," "She looks pretty good for being home-made," "Is it a horse or a cow?," all of them pretty good for Mrs. Dawson.

The third spot was the moment she put the key into the lock to open the grocery for the day. The insight of her humor progressed from, "Back to the salt mines," and "California here I come," to "Once more I offer my customers the opportunity to make Mrs. Dawson rich," and "If the bill collectors get any thicker, I am going to have to make this door wider."

She began to enjoy the game. In a few weeks she was adding her own moments to the original six. Gradually she came to feel kindly and delighted most of the time, and her face and personality began to glow with a kindly light.

She had succeeded in accomplishing the impossible. She was out of the ditch.

When her runaway husband finally slunk back home she told him, "Dawson, you're returning to a new woman. I'll expect you to act as though you liked her. If you don't, you'll please give me the pleasure of getting along without you again."

Mrs. Dawson had demonstrated that one can deliberately learn what is usually the result of unconscious conditioning, and that it is never as late as you think.

● *A Sense of Humor Is the Houseslave's Salvation*

It is entirely possible for a woman to plow through dismal years of marriage to the welcomed end, seriously handicapped by an acid disposition and a pick-axe sense of humor. It can be done, and many a woman has done it.

The mere fact that she did it merits a sort of cold admiration, and brings a clammy chill to one's spine.

A woman with a complaining disposition and with no sense of humor, pictures housework as a gigantic mountain pouring a constant avalanche of things to be done over a poor, tired, mortal struggling to pull herself up out of the debris.

And that is the kind of picture a woman should not dare paint—precisely because that is exactly what housework is. To meet it on that basis, to admit it, to label it with a big sign, "A Mountain of Work", is to live the life of a person hopelessly buried alive.

Nothing but a sense of humor and a pleasant disposition can pull a woman out of that workhorse role. Not even the kind of a husband can do it who regularly does all the dishes, all the cleaning, takes care of the children all the time he isn't at work; you simply don't find husbands like that. But you *can* develop a cheerful disposition and a sense of humor.

A sense of humor is a diversion; it is a quick release from the hot asphalt that is blistering your feet; it is a scurrying out through the barbed wire fencing you are in, into the fields and the woods at the side, to catch a breath of air, a sight of flowers, the song of birds, and the golden smell of pine.

It is the diversion of noticing little things that beckon you shyly and slyly for passing recognition, that leave you with a slightly lighter heart. It is the diversion of walking up a pleasant hill to make an objective, over-all assay of your world for what it is really worth; it is the determination not to miss the pattern of warm pleasant curves that hide behind the sharp angle of every situation.

A woman with a sense of humor can do just about anything and everything with it.

She can even manage to get some of it to rub off on a husband, a very fine accomplishment indeed.

● Rubbing Humor Off on the Husband

A thing you'll almost certainly find in a husband, if you haven't already found it in yourself, is a most troublesome obstruction sitting right in the middle of the mind, an obstruction standing in the way of anything you might try to do for him and with him. It also stands in the way of his doing anything with himself.

The obstruction is his blasted, bloated ego.

His ego simply occupies the whole place.

A person is, of course, nothing at all without some sort of an ego, a self. It is the nubbin to which the rest of him is attached. If it could remain what it really is, a nubbin, it would serve its purpose and still stay out of the way. But the human male it apt to blow up his ego too far, to an inordinate size where it simply takes up the whole space, and he is everlastingly strutting up and down before the mirror admiring its length and breadth.

A woman, before marrying, will do well to expect ego trouble in the husband, and verily she will seldom be disappointed. She is apt to find that her husband's ego has changed her status from being his wife to being a subservient priestess dragging endless gifts and sacrifices to an insatiable Buddha.

If you find *yourself* in that role, only a sense of humor can save you—and your husband. At least yours is the small comfort of being on the outside of it. You are not nearly as badly off as he is, in the middle of it, blown up by the uncomfortable distention of his ego.

If you can see yourself and your world through the perspective a sense of humor gives you, perhaps after a while you can get him to see himself and his world in the same way.

The male ego, so ridiculously constructed and out of plumb, more than anything else needs the perspective of a sense of humor to bring it down to scale, and to correct proportions. Once a man learns the trick of laughing and smiling *at him-*

self, he can prick the oversized balloon and let the wind out of it, and get relief at last by the deflation.

And you? Well, perhaps by the time you hear the hiss of the escaping air you've tangled yourself up in an inferiority complex, with the dismal feeling that you are about as small as a flea, incapable of handling *anything* in the way a human being should.

A sense of humor will straighten that out too, and bring you back up to size, convincing you that after all you are as worthy as the next, that your lot could be so much worse, that what you have now is a lark in comparison to what it could be.

In so very, very many ways, a sense of humor and a cheerful disposition are a woman's salvation. They are about the most important qualities for making an enjoyable companion out of an otherwise impossible husband, and a thrilling career out of the drudgery of housework.

Without a sense of humor she will discover that her life is devoid of any other kind of sense, too. Without it she will never enjoy anything, not even herself. If you can't enjoy yourself, what on earth can you enjoy?

3

Making the Most of It

It is very easy for a child to feel horribly abused and very sorry for itself.

The Fisher Family were baseball fans, and for a month had treasured tickets to a major league baseball game. But when the awaited day arrived, it started to rain in early morning and poured all day.

Six-year-old Billy, who naturally had his heart set on the game, felt miserably abused, pouted all day, and finally had a tantrum when Dad declared there was no use even going to the ball park. Billy's entire day was spent in deep remorse and self-pity.

We expect a child to react in that way.

But by the time adulthood is reached a person should be mature enough to accept the unfortunate turn of events and make the most of it without feeling morbid self-pity and abuse.

● *Why Women Seem Less Mature Than Men in the Matter of Making the Most of It*

In the doctor's office we see many more women than men who are there primarily because they feel abused, fairly dripping with self-pity, and unable to take it any longer. *Lacking the courage to make the most of it is the most common cause of emotionally induced illness in women.*

At first sight it seems a bit odd that this is true.

50

Biologically, women are more capable of withstanding stress than men and have endured greater hardship than men throughout history. Given equal circumstances, a girl would not need as much conditioning as a boy to meet life courageously.

There are two good reasons why women so frequently feel self-pity and lack courage to make the most of it.

First, the girl in American culture is not as well conditioned to meet life courageously.

Second, the conditions of life facing women and men are not equal; the woman generally has the more difficult problems and the tougher row to hoe. A woman *needs* more maturity than a man to make a go of it, especially the maturity of courage.

1. *The difference in conditioning the two sexes in courage.* The boy in our culture is conditioned in his reading, in athletics, in his recreation, in his associations, to "stand up and take it." It is manly to endure. But this quality is not expressly expected in a woman.

The boy is conditioned to meet the exigencies of life courageously; the girl is not. Boys, not girls, are taught "to take it on the chin."

The idea persists that the woman's is a protected lot, that she does not need courage. Courage, in our thinking, means valour in battle and physical courage, both of which actually account for an insignificant amount of the total courage living requires.

In our American culture the family protects its children from discomfort—especially the daughters—to a degree never seen before in history. So many of our girls meet so little discomfort and hardship in their youth they are inadequately conditioned to meet misfortunes later in life. There is no doubt that having to meet trouble and tribulation in childhood is the best conditioner for successfully meeting them later in life.

Nevertheless, in America we do see many magnificent women who, even though they were raised with a silver spoon in their mouths, are capable of tremendous courage. Somewhere along the line they manage to pick up the maturity of fortitude. They have the splendid pride of being personally greater than their misfortunes.

2. *A woman's problems require more maturity, including courage.* In Chapter 1 attention was called to the ways in which woman's life is more difficult than man's and calls for more maturity.

Men will argue this point *ad infinitum*. The best rebuttal is to invite them to take complete charge of the family and the house for a month. Most of them will be delighted to resume the male role at the end of that time.

Women's greatest problems are the children and the husband. Most children are usually something of a problem and so are most husbands. Of the two, husbands are frequently the much greater problem.

Husband problems can be aggravating, totally insoluble, and tremendously discouraging. It is primarily over husband trouble that women lose their courage to make the most of it, begin to feel terrifically abused and sorry for themselves.

The man with wife trouble can find relief and solace outside the home in his career. The woman cannot. Her marriage is her entire career. It is much harder for her to change the marriage she has started than it is for the man to leave a job he doesn't like. Her will to make the best of it gradually succumbs to the repeated blows of her situation until she is a beaten dog, thoroughly licked and broken in spirit.

● *Geraldine and Henrietta: Victims of Marginal Husbands*

Geraldine and Henrietta are good examples of two women whose marriage broke their courage and engulfed them both in self-pity and a feeling of abuse.

Geraldine's difficulty was obvious; her husband trouble was plainly visible to outsiders.

Henrietta's situation was equally difficult but her husband trouble was much less apparent. People were ready to blame her, rather than her husband.

There is also another difference in their two cases. Geraldine finally rose to a magnificent *tour de force* and managed to make the best of a bad situation. Henrietta, on the other hand, went down defeated and cowed, leading as futile and hopeless a life as any human being can, simply because she lacked the maturity to face the issue and make the best of it.

● **The Story of Geraldine and Joe**

Geraldine had plenty of good warning and good advice not to marry Joe from her parents and her closest friends.

Joe was an affable and agreeable enough fellow socially. He was handsome as well. He was capable of making a good impression on people he met.

His great immaturity was a distaste for work. He drifted from one job to another under the pretense that the job was not up to his capacity, with the air of a man who had a rendezvous with phenomenal success just around the corner. Joe began to find it increasingly agreeable to view his problem of making a living through the mellow glow of a glass of Bourbon and Scotch.

His romance with Geraldine inspired him, as one would expect, to higher resolution. He resolved to stick to a paying job and to stop drinking, resolutions that Geraldine welcomed but grossly overestimated.

Geraldine, like other women in a similar position, felt a motherly concern for Joe, and of course she loved him. She was confident that her influence and ability, along with his love for her, would make a man of Joe.

So they married.

Joe lived up to his flare for good intentions for the first few months. He zoomed into responsible husbandhood like a rocket. Then he burst prematurely into fireworks, and blackened out worse than before. He left his job and returned to the bottle.

At first Geraldine applied her wifely pressure gently and pleadingly. When that strategy failed she became critical and sharp; then, plagued with despair and frustration, she became downright nagging and mean. Joe resorted to drink more and more, to put his problems with Geraldine and his lack of work into a more comfortable perspective. He was drunk more often than sober, out of work more often than in a job. He became mean and ugly with Geraldine and the three children who had arrived in all too-rapid succession.

Geraldine had her own reasons for not getting a divorce. For ten years conditions grew steadily worse. The family lived in one of the poorest houses in town. The furniture was miserable, and appeared more beaten and scuffed than Geraldine. Once a beautiful girl, she now had the appearance of just having arisen from a sleepless night.

She felt as woebegone as she looked. She deeply regretted having married Joe. She was worried about the future of the children. She felt life had abused her, and self-pity tied her into a knot of frustration. She felt physically ill much of the time.

● Henrietta's Marital Frustration with Emil

Henrietta's marital troubles were of a kind that are generally more common than Geraldine's, a variety that many women meet in their marriages, and a kind that are not apparent or obvious to outsiders.

Emil would have been appraised by most people as being good husband material. People meeting him socially considered him agreeable, affable, likeable, and would not have imagined him to be what Henrietta soon learned he really was.

Unlike Joe, Emil was an excellent provider, much better than average, and he was always fair in sharing finances with Henrietta. Her allowance was usually more than adequate. Nor did Emil drink. He had all the earmarks of a good catch, at least the obvious ones.

It was not long after their honeymoon that Emil began to criticize Henrietta's homemaking efficiency with seemingly offhand remarks, which soon became more cutting and sarcastic. He was similarly critical of Henrietta's family. He laughed sarcastically about a hen house her gentle but somewhat inept father had built, and for a long time loved to bring the subject up for ridicule. He managed excellently in one way or

another to convey to Henrietta the idea that his estimate of
her family was considerably below zero.

He began to insist that she stay away from her family, and
especially to seek no advice from her mother. When advice
was needed, he would provide it.

Emil gradually assumed a masculine, dictatorial role and
lived more and more in his own world, away from Henrietta.
His only conversation with her was critical, derogatory, and
advisory. He went fishing and hunting whenever he wished,
always without her. With increasing frequency he went out
nights—to bowl, to Shrine meetings, to play cards with his
cronies. He took Henrietta out less and less often, and then
with reluctance. He spoke very little to her all evening except
to be humorous at her expense by telling people such things as,
"We never know at our house whether we are going to have
breakfast or lunch at dinner time" or, "Henrietta can sure
make a piece of meat good and tough better than anyone I
ever saw."

Henrietta tried to be endearing, tried to accept his idiosyn-
crasies and still be a companion to him. But Emil had never
matured to an adult level of consideration for human beings.
He was a hunting-and-fishing boy, with the pioneering spirit
of a ten-year-old boy scout in his blood. He had an early-boy,
belittling, opinion of women, and cruelty rather than tenderness of understanding for people, especially for the person
most intimately tied to his own life. It is really surprising how
many men like Emil there are in this country.

As the years went by Henrietta could not remember when
Emil had kissed her last or had shown the least sign of affection. She grew sexually frigid toward the man who gave her
only belittling criticism and not the slightest affection. This
lack of sexual response made Emil especially derogatory.

Living with Emil became more and more distasteful to
Henrietta.

Their four children became entirely her concern. Emil
merely came home to eat and go to bed, without taking any
active interest in the children except to keep them out of his
hair. Their problems were entirely Henrietta's problems, a

responsibility that she could not meet with anything like creative enthusiasm.

Henrietta bemoaned the direction her marriage had taken; she felt deeply abused by the ill will, critical attitude, and lack of affection of Emil. She felt caught in a horrible trap. Her future promised to be even gloomier than her present.

She felt deeply sorry for herself and became irritable as she became more hopeless; she smoldered with despair and frustration. She was always at the doctor's office because of emotionally induced illness. Her constant medical bills drew more of Emil's sarcasm, "Aw, you're always sick and belly-aching just like your mother."

Many women are caught like Geraldine and Henrietta in disillusioning marriages simply because they married a man whose great fault was his incapacity to conceive the vision of two people making out of life a rich, creative, and enjoyable experience; and because she was unable herself to convey that idea to him.

A man with the compensatory outlet of his work or business cannot appreciate how utterly and abysmally hopeless every minute of such a woman's life becomes. This marriage, which is such a miserable failure, *is her career.* Success in this endeavor is all she ever hoped to achieve, and it turns out to be infinitely worse than nothing at all. She is caught hopelessly, so very hopelessly, in a frightful trap. In a man's life there is very seldom anything comparable to the despair of such an outlook.

● The Courage to Make the Most of It

It is easier to advise women like Geraldine and Henrietta to rise above their situation and to make the most of it than it is for them in their bewildered and confused despair to follow that advice.

But as Carlyle said to Margaret Fuller when she made a statement to the effect that she accepted the universe, "Egad, you'd better."

Acting on the advice courageously to make the best of a bad situation may not be easy for them, but continuing to live as they are is even less easy. The possibility that the courage to make the most of it may improve their living is worth their one last great effort, is worth one final desperate attempt to push back into the sun, before succumbing completely to the awful despair of being sucked permanently into the quicksand in which they are caught.

They had the choice, of course, of getting out of their marriage by divorce. But neither Geraldine nor Henrietta wished to do that. Many women in their situation do not—sometimes for religious reasons, sometimes because to their confused, defeated minds there is only more defeat in the thought, "What will I do then, with two children?"; and very often because they are financially unable to start divorce proceedings.

What Geraldine and Henrietta both needed was to rediscover a fundamental type of courage with which the human race, and especially women, have always been richly endowed, a courage that has carried many a human being through dark, seemingly impossible places, a courage which Geraldine and Henrietta forgot that they, too, had. It is a desperate, an almost agonizingly desperate, kind of courage. But Geraldine and Henrietta could afford desperate measures, for their plight was desperate too.

Too often in psychotherapy, or in counselling women in Geraldine's and Henrietta's position, we fail to utilize the capacities—capacities that can only be termed *magnificent*— that most human being possess for carrying on with self-made compensations in the face of discouraging and seemingly hopeless obstacles. It is a quality humanity has had to forge for itself, hammering it out of cold metal, because of the insecurities that have always beset human life. It is one of humankind's most creditable and shining qualities, and through the ages, our most valuable attribute.

There have always been women like Henrietta and Geraldine; in fact, there are millions of women in far more difficult situations than they. The amount of misery women have suffered in the course of human history, the hopelessness of lives caught in the shallow patterns that all cultures have afforded women, has been far beyond that suffered by men.

It is for this reason—simply in the persistent need for it—
that women really have more basic courage than men. Men
have it too; every human being has some of it. But most
women have more of it than a man has.

She must not lay it aside and forget where she has put it.

● *How Geraldine and Henrietta Met Their Problems*

Both Henrietta and Geraldine needed courage to pull them
out of the unfortunate turn their marriages had taken, the
courage to make the best of it and create something good for
themselves in spite of the mess they were in.

They needed:

First, to stop feeling abused and sorry for themselves, to stop
spending all their moments bemoaning their black misfortune,
and stop turning their catastrophe over and over in their minds
all day and all night. They needed to start telling themselves
that since their lives had taken the turn they had, and since
the pitcher into which they had mistakenly poured their milk
was broken, there was nothing to be gained by weeping, wailing and self-pity. They needed to accept the fact that their
journey into marriage had taken them, not to the happy sycamore vale with its tinkling lotus pool, but instead had come
to this rock-strewn, barren desert. Feeling abused and bemoaning their plight would not improve the horrible spot they
were in.

They needed to call off their inner banshees and stop their
wailing from the rock-tops like a woebegone chorus in a Greek
tragedy.

Second, they needed to determine courageously to make
something out of it. Their marriage hadn't taken them to the
sycamore vale with its quiet tinkling lotus pool, but somehow,
in the desert of rocks to which they came, they needed to re-
arrange the rocks into a beautiful spot, to plant, cultivate, and
work the land, but above all, to grapple courageously to make
something good out of the situation.[1]

---

[1] **Grapple courageously:** the term used by Dr. Hornell Hart, *Autocondi-
tioning: The New Way to a Successful Life,* Englewood Cliffs, N. J.: Prentice-Hall, Inc., 1956, p. 42.

They could say to themselves, "Good heavens, you can still move, you can still breathe, there is still sky and air and a world of people and *you*. And most of all, you have the courage, if you'll only use it. Quit mulling over the marriage failure that got you into this, accept your husband at face value for the trouble in your life that he is, but don't give him the additional satisfaction of crying because of him. Go *on* in *your* life, go around him, let *him* stew in his own misery, but don't *you* stew. Do *something!*"

Henrietta and Geraldine were each in the position of the person whose house was afire and beyond the point where the fire could be extinguished. They had two courses open to them. One was to stand wringing their hands in distress and wail, "Woe! Woe! Why did this happen to me? Oh, pitiful me!" Or they could make the best of it and quickly save as many of their possessions as possible while there was yet time.

● *How Geraldine Found Courage*

Geraldine succeeded in doing just that by meeting her situation courageously. For ten years she had slipped deeper and deeper into the lowest depths of misery. Then one day she held a desperate conference with what was left of herself. She reminded herself that her time was spent worrying and hoping against hope that Joe could quit drinking and hold a job; she had futilely tried *everything* to make something of Joe; she admitted that she was pitying herself and feeling tremendously abused. There was obviously no further use trying to do anything with Joe or for Joe; that was merely beating her head against the wall, and she was gaining nothing by feeling abused.

Then and there she made a brilliant and courageous decision: From that moment on she was going to stop making Joe's failure the fulcrum of *her* life; she would no longer center her attention on Joe's problems nor on Joe being a problem to her. She would give him a home, certainly, but let the police worry about him; they did anyway. From here on she was determined to make her children's lives, and her own life, as pleasant, cheerful, and happy as she possibly could under the circumstances.

The core of her life underwent a simple but profound change. It was a change in emphasis and in outlook from a despairing, "What *can* be done to get Joe to quit drinking?", to a more hopeful, "What can I do to give the children a pleasant life. What can I do to give myself a lift?" On the surface, this may have seemed only a minor change.

A very little change in one's thinking can make a tremendous difference in one's living. Turning the dial of Geraldine's mind one-quarter turn in this seemingly simple way made the difference between night and day to her living.

The new orientation soon began to have its effect. Instead of being morose and complaining, Geraldine became cheerful, at first designedly and purposely so for the children's sake, later automatically so, as the habit became established. Living became a series of planned projects for the children and herself, projects that might introduce enjoyment (necessarily of an inexpensive sort) into their otherwise lean and threadbare lives. The children immediately sensed the changed attitude. So happy were they with the new Geraldine they caught fire themselves. Geraldine became a wonderfully effective and understanding mother simply because, with conscious effort, that was what she was trying desperately to be.

The financial part of Geraldine's reorientation wasn't easy. For a time she took in washing and ironing; later she found a part-time job typing. As the children grew older they helped with the housework and earning money, and by then Geraldine had a full-time job on the outside. She never forgot that her primary aim was to make the children's lives, as well as her own, as happy and interesting as she possibly could.

Geraldine became a different person. She had drive because there was something worth living for. Her face lost that haggard look and became cheerful and sparkling, full of the richness that she herself was creating.

Because of financial necessity, their enjoyments were inexpensive. They became masters at enjoying the little things.

In the evening, before clearing the table, they read many fine stories, and of their favorites — it seemed to fit them so well —was "Mrs. Wiggs of the Cabbage Patch", by Kate Douglas Wiggin.

The house itself began to show the change. Geraldine was often joyously surprised how clever she was in making something gay out of an old piece of half-wrecked furniture. When it came to decorating, she discovered that with a 25-cent can of paint she was as a veritable Michelangelo.

She saw to it that she and the children got out more to functions that were free. They all became active in Sunday School; she took active part and became an officer in PTA. Wherever she went she carried with her her endeavor to put the joy of living into the present moment. She became *the* person everyone was delighted to see because she made them feel better and more alive for having seen her.

Do not be misled. The thing Geraldine succeeded in doing wasn't easy. It was a desperate last effort in a sink-or-swim predicament. It called for every remnant of courage, creative ability, and will to put it into effect, that Geraldine could lay her hands on. Primarily it meant changing her attitude from one of miserable self-pity to one of courage, for making nothing into something, and as the attempt began to succeed and take shape, Geraldine changed from a melancholic complainer, careless about her appearance, to a remarkably pretty and wonderfully enjoyable person.

● Henrietta Did Not Find the Way Out

Poor Henrietta never found the courage nor the solution Geraldine did. She never caught the idea of giving the dial in her mind the same quarter-turn to a new attitude.

Henrietta stayed on the same path in her miserable life, growing ever more despairing in her self-pity, more sorry for herself, more abused, and gradually vindictive against everything and all the rest of the world. Good never came into her life because she didn't put it there. She never discovered where she had mislaid her courage.

● How Many Women Become Chronic Complainers

Geraldine and Henrietta both had cause for dissatisfaction and self-pity. But there are many women who are dissatisfied without sufficient reason, merely because they have allowed themselves to become chronic complainers. They are the authors of their own dissatisfaction. They grow sorry for themselves to the point where they can think of little else.

Sally was such a woebegone, self-pitying, dissatisfied, complaining female without sufficient cause. It was she who made her own life miserable, and not her life that made her miserable.

Sally had been a responsible secretary in the State Department in Washington. Early in World War II she met an army captain. They fell in love and married, and by the end of the war Sally had two children and was living in a trailer in a Midwest city. She didn't like living in a trailer, she didn't like bringing up children in a trailer—she didn't like raising children, period. She didn't particularly care for the Captain anymore. She certainly didn't like the Midwest, nor the city she was in. She wanted, most of all, to be a secretary back in Washington.

The more dissatisfied and self-pitying she became the more the Captain hovered over her. Frankly, he loved Sally.

The captain was a typical hovering husband.

The hovering husband is almost as great a domestic calamity as the disagreeable husband. He kills with *too much* solicitude, with overattention, with too intense anxiety for her welfare. He is so perfectly tuned to his wife's welfare that he picks up and magnifies all her static as well as her overtures. His hovering attitude appears to be a very desirable quality at first, then turns out to be tanglefoot flypaper that completely traps her in its sticky mess. He utterly spoils his wife. She responds by finding items for him to be concerned about. She begins to play on him as on a harp, dismal chord after dismal chord. It becomes very easy, even in an otherwise sensible woman, to be sucked into an attitude of boundless self-pity by a hovering husband.

The corroding combination of her own dissatisfaction and

the concern of her hovering husband gave Sally such a severe emotionally induced illness she needed to be hospitalized.

Fortunately for Sally her doctor treated her by showing her what her physical trouble was, what it was coming from, and how to overcome it, instead of the usual method of sending her home with pills for an ailment. Part of Sally's treatment was having to read the Pollyanna books, the story of a girl who played a game of finding as many good things as possible every time something bad occurred. The doctor also explained the cause of Sally's illness to her husband and explained the contribution of the hovering husband.

With Sally alerted to the necessity for finding satisfactions rather than dissatisfactions, awakened to the importance of making the most of one's situation, and with the Captain alerted to the necessity of being sensible rather than overattentive to Sally, the two of them began living together in a way productive of happiness. Today they live in a new modern home of their own, and Sally finds every day worth the endeavor and effort she puts into it.

● Loss of Courage May Lead to a Reactive Depression

When a person loses every vestige of his courage, is completely stuffed with remorse and self-pity, he develops very frequently what is termed a reactive depression. In such a depressed state the person is completely incapacitated, incapable of following through with any work, unable to do anything except sit around and moon and cry.

There are degrees of depression, from a faint dissatisfaction with oneself to a completely abysmal renunciation of everything, especially oneself. In such a last-ditch frame of mind a person becomes entirely helpless, unable to work, to eat, to think, to go on, and is a likely candidate for suicide. Men commit suicide more often than women.

Depressions are possible at any age. If a person becomes convinced by people's continual attitude toward him that he is a nincompoop, and he becomes increasingly aware that everything he tries is accompanied by failure, his self-confidence is jolted. With the first jolt he reels and staggers, but recovers again on a slightly lower basis of self-esteem and courage. After a series of such blows to the solar plexus, what little self-esteem remains drops to somewhere near zero. The person is of no use to himself or to others until his confidence and his courage are built up again, a thing which miraculously happens in most cases of depression.

A common age for the development of depressions is about the time one rounds fifty. On completing half a hundred years of living one naturally questions one's accomplishments, especially in the light of what one had hoped to achieve when young. The expectation of what life would amount to at fifty appeared so much more magnificent at twenty than it has turned out to be, that it is easy to feel deeply chagrined. The realization that so much of life is over and so poorly dealt with, the feeling that what is ahead will be only a further descent, a further gradual failure, increasingly insecure, opens the door to the feeling of utter futility.

In women the fact of the menopause, the end of the fertile productive phase of life, strikes home. Similarly in men the waning of their sexual libido and the beginning of loss of their sexual powers constitutes an additional blow to their ego.

So many women go into a depression around the age of fifty not so much because of the hormone change of the menopause, but because that is the time in one's life when one is very apt to become acutely aware of what life has not been and what it can never be. It is a time when one can easily feel discouraged by one's lack of accomplishment, and can readily feel a futility in regard to the future. It is around fifty that self-confidence and courage are apt to sink to a low ebb.

● The Earthy Type of Courage

The earthy kind of courage that depends on our own strength is fundamental and all important, and we must not forget it. One simply must stand up against the hard moments and, in hand-to-hand combat, wring from each disagreeable episode the satisfying compliment that we are superior to the ill fortune that hits us.

On one thing we must never let down our guard: We must never stoop, for one moment, to the ignominy of feeling sorry for ourselves. Rather we must act, in the face of difficulty, with an earthy courage that gives us a pure, inner gladness; we must realize that the strength lies in us to endure, to make the best of it, and to make the best a worthy accomplishment.

I have seen many magnificent, unsung heroes and heroines, like Geraldine, who have fought a courageous and successful fight against the stupendous odds that darkened their lives, winning out through difficulties that make the courage to fight a military battle insignificant by comparison.

● Janet—A Woman of Magnificent Courage

One such person was a woman who was permanently invalided by an unfortunate series of bodily diseases.

In her teens and early twenties, Janet's future was more rosy-colored and glamorous than it is for most people at that age. She was beautiful, vivacious, charming, intelligent. She was the kind of person everyone instinctively loved.

Just as she was about to be graduated from college with honors, Janet was stricken with pulmonary tuberculosis. After three years in a sanatarium, suffering through several operations, she was finally released. She returned home with a joyous expectancy, intending to salvage some of the old pieces and bring a purpose and direction back into her life. Instead of that she became woefully ill with rheumatoid arthritis. After years of suffering, it left her in such a hopelessly crippled state that she was unable even to feed herself, and permanently unable to walk or to get out of bed by herself. Her own funds and her family's funds being exhausted, she became a charge of the State. She needed to be confined to the barren gloom of an institutional ward, fed and lifted out of bed periodically by an attendant.

If anyone ever had a sufficient excuse for throwing in the sponge, giving up the fight once and for all, and bemoaning her lot, it was Janet. No one could have blamed her.

But the thing she did, the miracle she accomplished in herself, was as wonderful as if there were a sun giving just the right degree of warmth to the earth so that there could be life.

She became a sun giving out a glow of warmth and cheer
that actually, as I shall tell you, went over the whole world.
She herself became life, building a worthwhile existence in her
mind that seemed to live outside and away from the poor body
that was so very useless it could not even move. The bed in
which her misshapen body lay became a cheerful greenhouse of
pleasant thoughts that she cultivated and grew in tremendous
abundance and dealt out in large bouquets to everyone who
came near.

Many people who had never known Janet except through
someone else, came regularly to bask in her light, knowing very
well they were not there to cheer *her* up, or to help *her* pass
her time, but because she gave *them* something of tremendous
value, and sent *them* away loaded with more than they could
carry. Three different people volunteered to take her dictation
and type her letters to a growing society of bed-ridden unfortunates all over the world. She knit this society into an inter-
corresponding group of which she was the brilliant hub. The
motto of this society was not at all flowery nor verbose; it was
functional, direct, and effective like the society itself; "Give the
other fellow a lift, and quit worrying about yourself."

I asked this crippled woman one time how she had managed
to generate all this courage and make such a truly remarkable
and valuable life for herself with so very few materials. Her
answer was:

> I realized, above all, that I had to accept without
> a murmur the physical state I was in. It was fright-
> fully plain that it would only make matters worse
> to crab about it and to feel sorry for myself. Clearly
> there was nothing to do but to live with what there
> was left and make the most of that. I still had a mind,
> I still had eyes that could see and smile, I still had a
> mouth that could talk—and that was *all* I had. I was
> determined to use what I had in living as well as I
> could. See?

She smiled. I went away feeling proud to be a member of
the same human race Janet belonged to. Everyone went away
from her feeling that too.

A man who lives down at the end of my street put it much the same way. He had had more trouble in his life than any other ten people I ever knew. He was entitled to be sour and vindictive. Yet he came up the street (when he was able to walk) cheerfully whistling softly, greeting people with a pleasant "How do you do" and stopping to converse happily with his friends.

I stopped him one morning and said, "Cy, you *are* a wonderful man. With all the trouble you've had you are nevertheless the pleasantest man on this street. How do you do it?"

"Well," he said, "when all this trouble started, I sat down and thought for a long time. Finally I stood up and I said to myself, 'Cy, you might just as well cooperate with the inevitable and make the most of it.' And that is what I've tried to do—just simply to cooperate with the inevitable."

And Dale Carnegie and others put his phrase into a book.

Courage "to make the most of it" is an essential part of a good life that every woman must strive to mature in. She must expect that her world will deal her some hard, underhanded blows. And when ill fortune comes she must have a mature attitude that will allow her to rise above facts that she cannot alter, and endeavor to create something as fine as possible out of her troubles, instead of bemoaning her lot and feeling sorry for herself.

This courage lies innate in every woman if she will only search it out and cultivate it. Whatever comes, whatever insoluble problem arises, there always remains the final solution of taking inventory of the good that still remains, of assessing the increments of good fortune that still stand amid the ruins, and proceeding courageously to make the most of it.

4

Meeting Adversity and Being Flexible and Adaptable

More About Maturity No. 2

I. MEETING ADVERSITY

An important part of *Making the Most of It* is being able to meet the major catastrophes which are bound to occur in everyone's life, such as the death of a very loved one, or the loss of all our possessions and home.

Many people break up emotionally under the blows of adversity and never fully recover their stability.

It is when we are confronted with the dead face of our beloved, or the charred ruins of our home, that our philosophy of life shows its worth. *Our philosophy of life represents the sum total of our maturity.*

• Lives of Ease vs. Lives of Adversity

The security and ease enjoyed by the great American middle class is an unusual and unique phenomenon in world history. Most of us Americans have very little conditioning in our past experience to help us meet a crisis should catastrophe suddenly strike.

The vast majority of people in the world have always lived under conditions of great misery and deep poverty—as the people of China do today.

It is difficult for an American to believe and to grasp the picture that today over *400 million* Chinese live in single-room huts with dirt floors, with no windows or doors other than a simple opening, no fire except an open grate, that they are usually without sufficient food, and often without any food at all.

It is even harder to realize that such a state has been the lot of the majority of people throughout history, that most people (people like you and me) who have ever lived have been miserable, poverty-stricken, disease-ridden and engulfed in endless misfortune; their stomachs always empty before new food was found, with new woes piled on the fire before the old had burned out.

It is easy also to forget that in this great mass of suffering people, it has been women who have had the hardest lot, numbly bearing children and giving up the dying; their only privilege that of affording a recreation for the men, hardly considered to be human beings, not worth an education if one were to be had, not deserving even the few freedoms available, never considered seriously to possess human feelings, living the lives of domestic and sexual slaves.

Such is not at all an exaggerated picture of the life that the majority of women have had to lead through the course of the world's history.

In their average week, these people, both men and the women, have suffered more mental and physical discomfort than the average American meets in a lifetime.

The total amount of adversity that has been lived down by these billions of men and women merits the finest commemorative monument—the finest by far—that human beings have ever created to honor and commemorate anything. Their achievement lacks the glamor and brilliance of the people history remembers, but in terms of sheer effort, in terms of carrying on despite unbelievable odds and suffering, for simple, dogged magnificence, it stands as the greatest single accomplishment of any part of the human race.

- **"No Life Is So Hard but. . . ."**

These people are conditioned "to take it" from the moment they are born. *The only thing* that makes their lives any easier is the way they take it.

Ellen Glasgow wrote, "No life is so hard but you can't make it easier by the way you take it."

Learning "the way to take it" is, of course, developing a maturity.

Most of us are poorly conditioned to meet adversity by the very easy state of our living. When adversity does come many of us are bowled over and pitifully unable to carry on effectively.

The conditioning "to take it" in the lives of the miserable billions is largely an unconscious process of which they are not cognizant. But in people whose lives are relatively easy, conditioning must be a deliberate and conscious learning process, and the opportunity to learn this improved lesson comes to so few people.

The physician who is present when a wife, a husband, or a child dies, or is constantly having to tell people that a loved member of the immediate family has a fatal malady, sees people react in all manner of ways, immaturely and maturely.

He sees people like the man who had been completely incapacitated and unable to work for a year because of emotionally induced illness. Three months before this man became incapacitated, his wife died; a month later his son was killed in an automobile accident. His reaction to his adversity was not only a great self-pity, "Why did this have to happen to me," but also a futile and unrealistic rejection of the events that had occurred, "Why couldn't my wife have been saved, why couldn't my son have been spared?"

- *Conditioning the Maturity of Rising Above Adversity*

The maturity of having the courage to make the best of it, or "the way to take it," can be conditioned by conscious effort, just like any of the other maturities. Those of us to whom adversity is not a constant part of our lives must condition ourselves in that way in order to be ready with "the way to take it" when catastrophe hits us.

● **Teaching Yourself to Meet Adversity**

Let us see how you are to go about conditioning yourself.

When you have a moment to yourself, as when you are lying in bed not sleeping, plan how you would act, or react, if a major calamity were to strike.

Imagine yourself the victim of some major misfortune. Lay the cards on the table; deal yourself a very bad hand to see what you would do with it. Say your husband passes away suddenly in his office; or your daughter is fatally injured in an accident on her way to school.

To make your cup of adversity really overflow, assume that they are *both* taken at once, that your husband and your daughter are fatally injured as they drive downtown. Such a blow of fate, in many of its many possible variations, might conceivably happen, mightn't it?

Just *thinking* about it makes your breath come hard, your heart beat faster, and your head feel a bit woozy. You can readily believe that if the tragedy were actually occurring your physical reactions would be much more intense and much more severe.

Immediately on being told of the tragedy you would be seized by the physical manifestations of the emotion of fear, mixed from the very beginning with the emotions of grief, and turning completely into the latter as the immediate shock wears off.

● **Emotions Are Physical Phenomena**

These emotions *will* occur. You must expect them. You cannot avoid them. You can talk yourself out of a notion when a crisis arrives, but you can't talk yourself out of the immediate emotion.[1]

---

[1] Once an emotion seizes you, regardless of whether it is pleasant or unpleasant, the only further emotional control you have is by means of *the*

It is well to know that the physical reaction (which *is* the emotion) *will come.* Be prepared for it so that *it* will not unnerve you.

At the moment of such a crisis *the event* pulls the trigger that brings on the emotion. Unless one knows just what is going on inside oneself—that it is the emotion one is feeling and nothing serious—it may, and often does, increase the apprehension and alarm of the victim.

At first, this emotion of fear, turning rapidly to grief, causes you to draw in your breath in incredulous alarm; the next moment you exhale forcibly, your respiratory rate increases but is shallow, your chin drops but your lips tighten, fear pounds in your temples and chest. You will feel an unbearable constriction like a mighty, rejecting "NO" pulling the muscles of your chest and diaphragm. As you are trying to grasp the full and awful reality of what has happened, a lightheaded wave of numbness moves over you, and a heavy tiredness flows into all your muscles, your chest, into your arms, your legs, your abdomen. Your stomach becomes four great knots pushing up into your throat. Your hands and legs tremble, perhaps not outwardly, but certainly inwardly.

These feelings you cannot avoid. But do not be alarmed by them. These feelings *are* the emotion unavoidably triggered by the event.

Starting at this point you may work out your own strategy and mature attitude for meeting your catastrophic situation. If you are in doubt as to how or in what direction to proceed, let me give you some help. Perhaps I can suggest some idea of the direction a mature attitude should take in such a situation.

● First of All, Accept the Fact

First of all, think and say to yourself, "This has happened. The deed is done. It *is* now as it is. I must accept the fact. I

---

attitude you take, the thinking you do at that time which determines in great extent the *next* emotion you have. See Chapter I of the Author's, *How to LIVE 365 Days a Year,* Englewood Cliffs, N. J.: Prentice-Hall, Inc., 1955.

must admit the awful, inevitable finality of it. I am *not* going
to get out of hand with unnecessary frenzy or hysteria."

Maintain that thought firmly and calmly if possible; if at
first you do not succeed, then fight for self-control fiercely,
because a loss of control would throw you into a sobbing, hys-
terical heap, your face in your hands, crying in anguish, "No, it
can't be. It can't be. It simply can't be. Tell me it isn't so!"
Such a reaction would do you no good, and it is not any more
"natural" than the one described in the paragraph above. It
solves nothing but only makes new problems. It changes the
situation from the quiet, serious fact it is into a self-defeating
orgy of anguish that *is really self-pity*.

Collect yourself then and assume the determined attitude, "I
must accept what has happened, bravely. I am woman enough
to meet what has happened."

And assuredly you *are* woman enough to meet what has happened. Human beings, women, billions of them, have had to
meet just such catastrophes before, and the great majority have
met them admirably and with tremendous courage. This is the
quality that human beings, and women more than men, possess
in a crisis. Assure yourself of that—that you, too, are one of that
great battalion of brave women who have risen admirably
above their affliction in the moment of great crisis.

● Forming the Sustaining Attitude

Having met the first rude shock, you have then to form the
attitude that will guide you like a golden light through the dark
situation into which you have suddenly been thrown; a situation that may seem impossible at the moment, and impossible
of a good solution.

You have already accomplished the most difficult and most
important step by coming successfully and grandly through the
initial shock. Now you must use the attitude that makes it
possible to rise in some real sense above the awful reality that
presses down on you.

Out of the very ruins of the catastrophe you must pick up

the compensations to carry you through, to turn a bitter defeat into some sort of victory.

The exact form this supporting attitude will take will depend to a great extent on your particular background and your particular genius.

Changing bitter defeat into some sort of victory. I have never seen a more inspiring example of someone turning a major defeat into a grand victory than a young mother who was suddenly faced with the death of her husband.

Perhaps the attitude she formed to carry herself through had already been prepared in her mind, or perhaps she created it as she stood numb and immobile for several minutes after being told her husband had passed away. She stood perfectly quiet after I told her.

Tears welled into her eyes, but her face remained inscrutably calm and impassive. For several minutes her eyes focused on nothing, or perhaps they were looking into the secret places of her heart. *

Then through her tears came a wonderfully sweet and genuine smile. She spoke simply and slowly, pausing thoughtfully between every sentence:

> Paul was a wonderful man. It has been a great privilege to have been able to live with such a person. I guess it's up to me now to give these children the same wonderful spirit he always would have given them. He would want me to bear up and to go on just as though he were still here. And I am going to keep him and his influence here by trying to be as he would have been. I have lived with him for many years. He has given me so much. And now I guess I am going to have to give the children and other people the same spirit he gave me, and that he gave them.

She did exactly that.

Behind her simple straightforward speech was a profound maturity and a wonderful philosophy of life.

From that moment on she lived her attitude. You may be sure it wasn't as easy as she made it seem. Undoubtedly she was being wrenched by greater turmoil than she showed outwardly, and yet I am inclined to believe that even inside she was meeting it as courageously and successfully as she was outwardly. At least I am sure her outward calm provided an anchorage for whatever inward distress she had.

She gave herself warmly and brilliantly to the children, just as he would have done. To everyone around her she showed the same warm spirit of an outstandingly wonderful personality.

I hadn't known her before the tragedy. She must always have been a magnificent woman. But after it she certainly was a jewel in any gathering she attended. It was always a pleasure to meet her. She was making her life good, as she was everyone else's she met. Amiable, cheerful, pleasant, and with a brilliant mind, she could turn an insignificant day for anyone into something that was worth living merely by means of a few minutes' conversation.

How sensible and extremely mature her attitude was! If it ever occurred to her to rebel against the fact, to pound her heart with a useless, "Why did it have to happen? Why couldn't he have lived?," she showed no sign of it to anyone else. She accepted the catastrophe without that useless, agonizing pain that goes with listening to the awful, empty, reverberating answer that returns like an echo when one asks futile questions of that kind.

She sensed the fact that no one is dead whose influence goes on in other living beings. In one grand moment of genius she raised a memorial of immortality to her husband's memory. She made the influence he had exerted a part of herself, adding her own fine increment to her husband's admirable qualities. The personality that had been his was now alive in her and she would pass it on to her children and they in turn to others. This is actual immortality. If we should choose to examine ourselves we find that so many of our traits, so much of our outlook, our reactions, even our little mannerisms and peculiarities, come from a grandfather we knew well, a grandmother, from our mother or father. We have in us, if we knew it, increments from ancestors who lived hundreds of years before us.

● *Work, an Antidote for Adversity*

When her husband is taken by death, or some other catastrophe occurs, a woman is fortunate if she has a demanding job in which she can lose some of the sharp sting of the blow she has received.

If she has a family of children at home her opportunity for work is already available. But if the family has grown up and left home, the widow may very well be plagued with too much time for useless remorse and self-pity.

In such a case she will do well to find an outside job, either in business or industry, or as a voluntary worker for some service organization. Or, lacking specific abilities, she may return to school to train for a new career.

● *The Strength Afforded by Religion in Time of Adversity*

Through the ages most people's great comfort and source of help in time of great trouble has always been religion. When catastrophe strikes, people the world over seek Divine Help in prayer. When the chips of life are down, Mohammedan, Jew, Hindu, Buddhist, Christian—all turn to a help higher than man, each one in the way he has been taught. A great comfort and solace comes to him who sincerely addresses his Maker, whether he prays in Arabia, India, Europe or America.

It is not for us to say that any one of them alone holds true converse with God. Only a bigot would claim that prayer is answered only if it is conducted within the tenets of one certain creed.

The exact form of your own religious approach in a time of adversity will depend, of course, upon your religious background. Whatever your particular religious background may be, do not neglect it. You may well discover, as many people have before you, that you have not experienced the great richness of your religion until you come to it in the hour of great need. If you too make this discovery, then your adversity has indeed been changed into something which is good; and a defeat has been turned into a victory.

● *Condition Yourself to This Maturity*

Certainly the history of the human race is richly filled with indication that God helps those who help themselves, and that to no inconsiderable degree God's help *is* the help people make for themselves, utilizing the abundant raw materials, including intelligence, that the Creator has placed at man's disposal. Answers to prayer are often more intricate than man's poor mind can decipher and perceive.

Every person needs to form a mature attitude that will direct his course when a disagreeable emergency arises. He needs to condition himself by thinking ahead and laying a plan, utilizing in his plan all his resources, including his religion, so as to be ready when misfortune strikes.

Unless you form such a mature plan of action, and condition yourself to a mature attitude by thinking it through ahead of time, you may well be caught short and thrown for a loss, as a football fan would say. And as your life goes on, this may well turn out to be the play that lost you the game.

II. BEING FLEXIBLE AND ADAPTABLE.TO.CHANGE

Another important aspect of *Making the Most of It* is being able to remain flexible and adaptable to change.

The conditions of our living, everybody's living, are constantly changing. Unless we have the attitude that allows us to change agreeably and flexibly as conditions change, we sooner or later run our heads into a wall of frustration.

The day may start out well enough, but by evening we learn that Jimmie has completely failed in college; or husband has lost his job, or he is being transferred from the town in which you have lived 20 years to another town 1000 miles away; or the house redecorations on which you had set your mind cannot be done because you have to borrow money to pay your income tax.

Everything in the world and in human living is in a state of constant change. Automobiles change from something you climb up into and sit upright in, to something you crawl down into and crouch over in. The trees in the yard blow down. The rain fills the cellar with water. Salt refuses to pour. Milk turns sour.

Our living will be miserable if we allow ourselves to become frustrated and upset by change instead of meeting new circumstances with the attitude, "*Of course*, I will make the best of it."

The idea isn't that we take things sitting down, or that we lie down and let everything and everyone run over us.

It is part of maturity to strive to make conditions better. But it is also the part of maturity to adjust to the inevitable circumstance rather than allow ourselves to be upset with childish grief and frustration.

● *Disciplines for Keeping Oneself Flexible and Adaptable*

It is well as you go along from day to day to exercise a few disciplines to keep yourself flexible and adjustable.

1. Expect sudden changes in the status quo. Realize that changes are bound to occur, that they are absolutely a normal and inevitable part of existence. Expect bad luck occasionally, and verily you will not be disappointed.

That does not mean you have to maintain the attitude of a crepe-hanger. You are not to sit around wringing your hands and sobbing, "Something is going to happen, but I don't know what it's going to be."

You roll up your mental sleeves and say, "O.K., let changes come, let things pop. I'm ready for them, ready for anything that can possibly happen."

To expect that the *status quo* is stable is merely an excellent ride to a big fall.

Be realistic. Have an attitude prepared for change.

2. Avoid the all-or-none perfectionist attitude. Do not picture your world as an ideal castle of absolute perfection, where everything you have must be completely flawless, not a thread on the rugs, not a speck of dust in the corner behind the stove. Don't think yourself the wisest, the brightest, the most comfortable, the most entertaining person in the world, with superlative ideals of honor, virtue, perfection in love, utterly good, maintaining yourself in a state of impeccable lustre. Leave yourself enough room to be human.

Don't try to maintain an impossible standard that is sure to keep you unhappy. If you do, your first great irritations will come when you expect the same perfection in your husband or children; the second when you find a scratch on the highly glistening, immaculately polished, mirrored surface of your escutcheon; your greatest degree of unhappiness will come from the terrible (and silly) effort you will have to make all your life to keep your world in its perfect shape; and your final breakdown into sheer frustration, so deep it will be the first *perfect* thing you ever achieved, will come when untoward circumstances beyond your control wreck your castle and sweep its pieces into the dust.

This all-or-none attitude, this idea of everything having to be exactly perfect "or I can't stand it," is a selfish, egotistical, immature attitude. It is an immature attitude to hold in the sort of world in which we human beings live.

Cultivate the attitude of enjoying that which is not perfect, rather than spoiling enjoyment by trying to be perfect. You can do a good job without needing to feel let down if you have not achieved perfection.

3. Do without one thing every day. A neat little trick to keep you conditioned for eventualities, is one that was advocated by no less an expert than William James.

Every day get along without *one* thing you think you need. For instance, give up smoking for a day; or go without make-up, or without this, that, or the other thing you think you can't get along without.

I really doubt whether you will try this trick. Not that it wouldn't be good for you, but I suspect you are a woman who, like most, already has so much on her mind, such an endless backlog of things undone, that one more thing is just the straw it takes to break an already sagging back.

But at least try it once in a while. Or better yet, get it started as a *family* project to be indulged in every Tuesday, say, or Saturday. As a family project the trick becomes *fun*. Really

good fun. For instance, the family of the Wyalusing Conference
had a day every two weeks when every member of the family
did without mother's meals—no restaurants, either!—but foraged
for food on their own and *cleaned up their own kitchen mess
and dishes.* It was fun and a good discipline for all. It seemed
to be rather a back-handed penance for mother since she was
relieved of one of her major duties that day. But of course she
made up for it by catching up on yesterday's leftovers, or last
week's ironing, and last season's cleaning the closets. The rest
of the family gloried in the kindly thought that their sacrifice
was making it pretty soft for her. But let them think so; mother
is always like that. And the next day the whole family appre-
ciated mother's meals (and mother) all the more.

4. Avoid being a stereotyped fuddy-duddy. It is a great
help to more agreeable living, not to let yourself get so stereotyped in your likes and dislikes, habits and desires, that you
froth yourself into a lather, or flutter yourself into the jitters,
everytime one of the minutiae of living blows up in your face.

The bread at breakfast, let us say, pops out of the toaster a
shade or two overdone, browner and harder than your individual bureau of standards prescribes. Go ahead, eat it and like it!

Someone (mother, of course) forgot to put the salt on the
table. For once eat the meat without it; everyone else seems
to be satisfied with what seasoning there is on the meat.

Or, let us suppose, the day is wet when you wanted it dry
and sunny. Change your plans and your wishes, and want it
wet.

You go to church and the minister belays you with the same
theme he used six weeks before, with no improvement in his
stories or his references. Go along with him; enjoy it by sup-
plying in your own mind what he lacks in his, giving the sermon
the help it needs to be a success. Then as you leave the church
door, give the poor fellow the credit he deserves. Did you ever
try to cook up a fresh sermon every Sunday?

It is a ridiculous invitation to small frustration to let yourself
become a hopelessly stereotyped fuddy-duddy, to demand one
special brand or nothing, to insist on your own set of rules or

you don't play, to do everything your way or you go into a tantrum, to follow one kind of procedure or you blow a fuse.

This discipline we are proposing doesn't mean that you can't set yourself standards of excellence and strive to maintain them —whether it's a question of toast, the weather, sermons, or what-not. It simply means that you should not get into the rut of stereotyped habits so deeply that you can't pull out when fate deals you something less than you wanted.

5. *Roll out your sense of humor.* Above all, get into the habit of meeting the unexpected and perhaps unfortunate change with a sense of humor. If you don't, you will find that many a day will be turned into the sort of thing Ma Kettle meant when she said, "It's the kind of a day it ain't even worth gittin' dressed fer."

A friend of mine was a foreman in a plant that was on strike. It was his permitted duty to go into the plant daily to tend to some vital equipment. As he passed by the strikers milling at the gate, someone mistook him for a scab and with unerring aim threw an overdated egg at him, catching him just behind the ear. Wiping the mess off with his handkerchief, he smiled at those beside him. "Oh boy," he said, "the butterflies are sure big these days."

A career woman of my acquaintance took to marriage. New at housework, she was adapting very successfully to the astonishing fact that housework was much more difficult and overwhelming than she had ever imagined, or than anything she had ever done before.

Her first Saturday, far from being the day off to which she had become accustomed, was a hectic putting together of the unfinished work of the week, and included cleaning an accumulated pile of pots and pans. By 10 P. M. she felt she could blow the "all clear" signal. True, there were still a dozen things undone, but her week's experience told her that such items were an optimal, irreducible norm in housework.

The next morning, which was a Sunday, she made a final attempt to tickle her husband's palate. Her inexperience prompted her to prepare a breakfast of apple fritters, one of her

mother's great breakfast successes. Everything was going fine—
at least in a hesitant, jerky sort of way. The cookbook recipe
went together fairly well, the sliced apples were ready to play
hide-and-seek in the batter, when suddenly the pan of hot
grease burst into a furious blaze. For a few hectic minutes there
was no time for consternation. Smoke filled the house, and
the fire scorched and blackened the stove and the newly-painted
kitchen wall and ceiling.

The heroic measures finished, with the deep fat pan lying
blackened out in the yard, the opened windows letting the
smoke out and the cold air in, she collected herself and smiled
sweetly at her husband:

"There, honey, we have enjoyed apple fritters for breakfast
once and for all time, at least for quite a time. We are now
graduating to toast for breakfast. I know a very good recipe for
plain, simple, unadulterated, buttered toast."

Then, too, there was the friend who had to take a train trip
on business the day after Christmas. As he sat quietly and
silently in the observation end of the plush train, some affluent
men about him were engaged in conversation. For want of a
better subject, each in turn told what he would do with a
million dollars if it were suddenly given him. All had outlined
their plans, when one of them hospitably turned to my silent,
thoughtful friend, and asked, "And what would you do if someone were to give you a million dollars?"

My friend smiled wanly and remarked, "I'd use it to help
pay for the presents I bought for my family for Christmas, as
far as it would go."

6. *Always find and play up the compensations.* There is
one more discipline to help you adjust advantageously to
change.

When something turns up that is absolutely inevitable, but
nevertheless hard to take, enumerate to yourself (inventing
some points, if necessary) all the possible compensations in the
new order of things.

A wonderful couple of my acquaintance had fashioned a fine,
rich life for their family of four children out of a teacher's very

moderate salary. After the children had each gone out into the world a truly excellent adult, and the time came for the father to retire, the elderly couple found their savings would not allow them to continue living in the house and yard which through the years they had come to love, and in which almost every board and every nail held precious memories of their children's days.

At the conference which the two had on the matter, they admitted openly the financial situation that made the move to a small, inexpensive apartment necessary. But ever after that, they intimated to each other and to the children that they were moving because, as they put it, "It will be so much less housework for mother, so much less yard work for father, especially in winter with the snow, to move into a cozy little apartment just big enough for two, without even a car or garage to trouble with. Besides, it will give us something new in life, a refreshing change at a time when we need a little rejuvenation."

In a very genuine sort of way, going through life is like playing in a football game in which you are constantly carrying the ball. You are in mid-field and a bunch of big, bruising opponents is bearing down on you. You look quickly about, you see your opening, and you are dashing for it like a flash, twisting, turning, and slashing—and you are through! You are in the open! It's a grand feeling even though you have no audience to cheer your play.

The good player finds the openings.

5

Being Unselfish and Having
Consideration for Others

Maturity No. 3

● *Women Come by This Maturity More Naturally Than Do Men*

Being unselfish and considerate comes more naturally and more easily to a woman than it does to a man, simply because of her role of mother and homemaker.

In her relation to her child, the woman has a more unselfish attitude than is found anywhere else in human living. Traditionally a mother carries an attitude of consideration and understanding for other people. This attitude becomes a conditioned part of every woman, handed down from mother to daughter. It is taught her in so many ways, even in playing with dolls and keeping make-believe house.

All through life the woman is more able than a man to efface herself and her ideas in the give-and-take of marriage, and more able to discern the personality factors and needs that are such an important part of other people.

The conditioning factors in a man's life, such as the attitudes he gets from his father, the type of aggressive and assertive boy's play that he indulges in by custom, the retention in society of the belief that man is the hunter and the getter, the competitive school athletics, are only a few of the influences that place a premium on a man's being egotistical and selfish. He

84

must be interested in getting his hands on at least his share, and preferably a little more than his share, of the world's boodle and plunder.

Not that every woman is the quintessence of unselfishness and every man an egotistical beast! Heavens no! What we are trying to say is that the *tendency* toward unselfishness is more commonly found in women, and that most women more readily exercise consideration for other people than do most men.

● **Which Is the Most Important Maturity?**

It would be hard to say that any one maturity is more important than all the others, and to pick this or that one out for honor would be unfair and unrealistic. In this book we are not presenting the maturities in their order of importance.

If they must be graded in their order of importance, I would say *the key* maturities can be narrowed down to four, and I would grade these four in this order,

1. *Enlightened selfishness and consideration for others.*
2. *Making the most of it.*
3. *Self-reliance.*
4. *Having a predictably pleasant disposition.*

One is inclined to give enlightened selfishness and consideration first place because psychiatry has amply revealed that selfishness is the immaturity that does people most harm; and unselfishness the maturity that does them most good.

● **Why Children Become Little Selfish Monsters**

The average child is tremendously self-centered and selfish.

This selfishness is not any more "natural" to a child than unselfishness, unless by "natural" one means that it is the result of conditioning factors that are an inevitable part of early childhood.

And the same thing is true of all the immaturities. They are as much a conditioned type of response as are the maturities.

The selfishness so characteristic in children is produced by the very conditions under which children are reared.

Selfishness and egotism are not any more inborn than unselfishness and consideration for others, but are easily conditioned in the infant because of several factors. A child enters
the world neither with the idea of service to its fellow men,
nor with the thought that it is ruthlessly going to exploit the
services of others.

At birth the baby is a biological system that is motivated by
simple biological needs and equipped with a set of reflexes designed to fulfill those needs. The newborn baby represents six
pounds of organic needs and the sensations that occur when
those needs are not being met. This is the entire extent of its
first interests.

This is a perfect setup, you see, for the conditioning of egoism and selfishness.

The infant gets hungry, it becomes thirsty, it gets too cold or
too warm, it becomes uncomfortable because of its position,
it has a colicky pain in the abdomen. Its first reaction is a whimper, then it whines; finally, when the discomfort is acute enough,
it cries. Someone comes running with food or drink, with a
blanket, or a clean diaper. Why shouldn't the baby feel, as
one of its first conditioned impressions, that it is the center
of the universe, the central object for whose benefit all things
are done by all the forces that exist? Why shouldn't it get the
idea that it is just about the only, and certainly the most important, existing thing, and that there is nothing else that really
matters?

The baby represents the perfect setup for the conditioning
of selfishness and egoism, a conditioning that is practically
unavoidable. If you think such conditioning is avoidable, you
might figure out some other way of taking care of a baby; if
you can, I dare you to put it into practice.

Little wonder that we all start out as little self-centered
monsters whose own needs come first, and with the idea that
ours are the only needs that exist, that other people have no
needs, not even the need to sleep. A whimper sets the relief
machinery into motion, and a cry results in succor being rushed
to the scene.

As Madame de Girardin put it, "Self-interest attacks us from infancy, and we are startled to observe little heads calculate before knowing how to reflect."

After it has been conditioned to a state of almost perfect egoism, the infant is further conditioned to a state of excessive self-esteem and self-praise by the things people say and do around it. Why shouldn't a baby, surrounded by a host of drooling admirers, get a big head concerning its importance? How can it possibly avoid getting the idea that it represents all that is desirable and perfect? By early childhood its attitude has been conditioned to such comments as:

"My ma is purtier'n your ma."
"My pa ken lick your pa."
"My sled is faster'n your sled."

In late childhood, selfishness, and egoism are further conditioned by the competitive techniques so commonly employed in primary and secondary education, by which the good, the brilliant, the capable, the talented are rewarded for deportment, for scholarship, for athletic prowess. This type of conditioning most adversely affects the more brilliant and talented people, and in large part accounts for the fact that brilliant and talented people can sometimes be a bit insufferable and overbearingly egotistical.

Pity the poor child who is capable of running off with the honors and first prizes in all the competitions it encounters in the course of its school life. Such a child, who might otherwise have developed the maturity for making so much good of itself and its life, is only further conditioned to be so strongly egotistical and self-centered that it will probably never be able to condition itself to a more mature outlook. Very possibly its chances of leading a rich and enjoyable life have been ruined.

One might suggest that these competitions do help those who lose, and there are many more who lose than win. But the attitude that is conditioned in the loser is not one of unselfishness, but one of inferiority. A strong inferiority complex is similarly a self-centered emphasis on one's ego and one's capacities. It is a strong awareness of the self in a negative, regretting way. It is only a shade less bad than being strongly and boastfully impressed with oneself.

Selfishness is an early conditioning which to some extent, at least, is unavoidable. But certainly, if one is to grow up to benefit oneself and others, the individual must sooner or later be reconditioned to the maturity of unselfishness.

In many people, of course, the reconditioning to unselfishness never takes place, or takes place only partially and imperfectly, or in a warped sort of way.

Many people, especially men, remain childishly selfish all their lives. Such selfishness, along with a rotten disposition in the husband, make more marriages dreadful nightmares for wives than do any other two immaturities.

• There Are Varying Degrees and Mixtures of Selfishness and Unselfishness in People

Many men and women remain as naïvely egotistical and self-centered all their lives as a four-to-six-year-old child. One frequently meets executives, professional people, businessmen, office workers, laborers who are still pretty much in the "My sled is better'n your sled" stage.

Some people are so selfish and egotistical it is painful to be with them.

Others are less obviously selfish but can still be easily spotted. They love to talk about what *they* have done and what *they* have, like "I'll never forget the time I put a fresh traffic officer in his place . . . and I . . . and I . . . and I." Or, "I never saw an outboard motor perform like the one I have. Of course there aren't many outboard motors that are kept in the perfect shape mine is."

There are some who manage to coat their selfishness with a misleading veneer. Perhaps they have the social grace to allow someone to pass through the door ahead of them, or they have had the breeding to pass a glass to someone else before accepting theirs. But their thoughts are on and for themselves. Regardless of the desires of the others in their family they plan the type of thing, the kind of pleasure, the variety of recreation they themselves enjoy, going to the things *they* want to see, calculating every turn of events in terms of their own egos. You will frequently find them competitively comparing themselves with others. They brag about their work to fellow workers and delight in calling attention to someone who isn't doing a job as well as they. They love to call attention to their little superiorities, or to the relative inefficiency of their wives. They can manage, in mean little ways, to make their wives appear microscopically small and about as useful as a termite gnawing at *its* bank account.

● Enlightened Selfishness

The basic and fundamental reason for being unselfish is the purely selfish one that it helps a person more than being selfish.

Why deny this is a purely selfish reason for being unselfish? Most assuredly it is. Nevertheless it is the only good reason ever given for being unselfish. Even the old reason, so often given, that one should be unselfish because God decreed it, had the selfish motive behind it that sooner or later leading a Godly life will reap its just rewards, if not here then in Heaven. But unselfishness brings its own immediate rewards, here and now.

The more unselfish a person can be, and the more completely he learns to give others the same consideration he gives himself, the more he helps himself.

The best term I have ever heard for this type of unselfishness is *enlightened selfishness.*

Do not be so egotistical as to think yourself superhuman enough to be capable of pure unselfishness. But you may fully expect yourself to be capable of practicing enlightened selfishness, and that very richly.

There is a point where really effective enlightened selfishness becomes so seemingly pure as to look like unrewarded philanthropy. But a slim though always strong thread of self-interest always remains, never fear.

A mother sacrifices her comfort and her health for her children; but the children are hers, and giving them help means more to her than does her expendable self. A man giving his life for a cause that he believes more important than his own person is acting on the highest level of enlightened selfishness; he obtains by his sacrifice an ultimate satisfaction.

Enlightened selfishness returns more benefits than any degree of sacrifice that it might entail, and the more refined it becomes, the more it is worth to the individual.

● Consideration for Others a Part of Enlightened Selfishness

The very process of dealing with other people in as unselfish a way as possible implies that we must have consideration and understanding of their point of view and of their needs.

The very process of cooperating with people calls for a consideration and understanding of their needs which, in turn, brings us the awareness that these are people like ourselves. We develop the enlightened view that every other human being is a person like ourselves, endowed with the same feelings of love and hate, of joy and sorrow, of longing and desire for a better existence. We learn that these are persons whose rightful human heritage, like our own, is freedom from tyranny, freedom from injustice, freedom from preventable catastrophes, freedom from want, from fear, from malignant influences.

Once this consideration for others has begun in a genuine way with the people in our family, there is no barrier, except a lack of imagination, to keep it from including every and any human being on earth.

Consideration starts at home as a feeling for the inner person who resides in one's wife or husband and children—a desire to understand their problems, their possibilities, and to help them as we would ourselves.

From the family, consideration goes out into all the world.

● Enlightened Selfishness Actually Is the Basis of Our Life

We don't often stop to realize that EVERYTHING any one of us has, whether it is material, spiritual, or intellectual, we have as the direct result of other people. We have it because there was another man, another woman, many of them, in fact, who did this or that, who gave us the idea we are using now, the paper on which we are writing now, the chair we are sitting in, and EVERYTHING else we have.

We don't often stop to realize that one human being trying to live in this modern world of ours *entirely* on his own resources would present a miserable and pitiful spectacle.

● Our Lives Absolutely Depend on Others

It is fair to predict that if in some unusual way it would suddenly be decreed that everyone in this country must depend entirely upon himself, completely devoid of any article or any knowledge that required the help of someone else, only a handful of us could possibly be alive at the end of a year.

The only shelter any of us would have would be a cave or something we could make without tools. With no axe available, we could not cut down trees until we had learned to sharpen stone; our food would consist of what we could catch or what we might be able to find; cultivating a field would be out of the question without tools or knowledge. All of these things it originally took countless generations to develop. To make a fire we would have to learn the method of rubbing sticks or striking flint, for a simple match would be unprocurable.

The simple match we use to light a cigarette requires two dozen different enterprises and thousands of people cooperating for what turns out to be our personal benefit. The paper on which we write is the product and end-result of thousands of people working together; not only people living today, but persons who from ages past have helped add refinements to produce this perfect sheet of writing paper that we accept so easily today.

They are mostly unknown to us; the people who cut the pulpwood, the people who run the paper machinery, the people who make the machinery, the people who mine the iron ore, the people who make the steel to make the paper machinery, the people who contribute a hundred other things so that this sheet of paper might be made for us, people in Africa, Asia,

South America, Australia, and Europe. I have contributed more or less directly to this sheet of paper by giving medical attention to the people who make the machinery that makes this paper.

And yet the sheet of paper is a relatively minor item in our living.

The whole human enterprise is an amazing and complicated system of cooperation and mutual service. Everything we have —everything—represents the help and cooperation of another person.

To a considerable degree, each one of us is actually *forced* to a degree of cooperative maturity. Each one of us learns how to provide a service someone else needs so that we can buy the things we need that someone else makes. We are forced to mature in this to some extent, for the selfish reason of providing ourselves with a type of human living that is infinitely better than solitary survival in a jungle.

Realizing that mutual cooperation can accomplish all this, can bring us our homes, our autos, our meals, our entertainment, and a hundred thousand necessities and luxuries, we can begin to realize that the matter of cooperative endeavor between human beings can rise to even greater heights, can encompass more and finer varieties of mutual benefit than it already has.

It follows that in our own personal relations with our families, our friends, our business associates, cooperative endeavor can raise the level of our personal lives immeasurably.

Enlightened selfishness and consideration for others pays off on all levels of human living. It pays off first of all in our immediate families, and it pays off in our relations with the entire world.

● Selfishness vs. Enlightened Selfishness in the Family

Whether you are a man or a woman, the family is the unit to which you most genuinely belong. Here are the people most important in your living; to them you owe your loyalty, your greatest consideration, and everything you've got. The family is the center of your living. If it isn't, you've gone far astray. You are not only missing the boat, but you have let yourself and your family down.

The family is what you make it, and the most important ingredient that goes into its making is this same matter of unselfish consideration for others that must be as great and as genuine as your consideration for yourself. The success of your family will depend on the degree of mature cooperation and consideration the members of the family can develop among themselves. If one member is mature in this respect, the chances are the others too will develop the same maturity, for the example provided by one unselfish, considerate person so obviously illustrates a better way of living that it readily becomes contagious. One has only to experience unselfish living in action to be struck by the idea, "Well, this is certainly the way to live; why in the world haven't I been doing it?"

Families in which consideration and cooperation are as rare as feathers on a monkey, have no conception of the delightful joy of living in a family that is well stocked with that essential commodity. And *vice versa*. Families rich in cooperative consideration cannot visualize what a constant hell-on-earth the other type of family is.

The picture of the selfish family. The members of a family in which everyone is childishly selfish all think of themselves first, and are constantly doing the selfish things their egos impel them to do. The friction of egos in such a family is constant; they are forever rubbing each other the wrong way until they are sore; then instead of applying soothing oil, they follow with acid and arsenic until the soreness has become a wound. Then with glee they open the wound and reopen it until it festers. Dante's description of inferno is mild compared to the hell the members of such a family make for each other.

The center of agitation is, of course, the parents. They set the stride and the example. The children pick it up as the only demonstrated way of living. They see no other.

Sniping and taking pot-shots at each other is their constant, belligerent pastime. More intensive bursts of shooting occur at any time, any place; at the dinner table, in the living room, in the kitchen, in the bedroom, in the back yard, or in the front yard.

Verbal fighting becomes so habitual that it makes little difference whether visitors are about or not. Practically anything anyone says is met with disdain, contempt, sarcasm, or a snarl. No one ever says anything nice; in fact, nothing nice ever occurs to prompt such a remark. Every person in the family obstructs the others from satisfying their personal desires; the other family member is someone to be outwitted, to be talked down, to be put in his place. Often the altercations take on the air of a pack of wolves snapping and growling over a piece of meat. Or the family tension simmers down to the uneasy quiet of a bunch of thugs glaring at each other, wondering who'll start the shooting next. There may be a burst of fireworks out of a clear sky as someone suddenly becomes aware his ego has been ravaged, or suddenly realizes someone has done him dirt, fouling up his selfish designs. Or the fighting may develop with a mighty crescendo from an inconspicuous skirmish.

"I don't see why you should get an outboard motor right now when I need a dishwasher in the kitchen."

"Good heavens, my mother never had a dishwasher. She wasn't so lazy she couldn't wash a few dishes. You women nowadays don't know how to work. You've got to have a million dollars worth of junk around to do your work for you. I wish I had it as easy as you have. You ought to have to do my work for a day."

Well, that does it.

The heavy artillery is brought up. The cavalry deploys. The engagement develops into a major battle with attack, counterattack, flanking movement, and on into the night under the light of star bombs and bursting shells.

The battle is replete wtih divertive and discursive tactics, a favorite strategy being to reintroduce all the old-time fights, opening up all the old wounds with sharp, pointed reminiscences of topics that should have been swept up into the dust heap and forgotten long ago.

No one wins, not even the devil. Sheer weariness from reiteration forces the end—no, not really an *end*—only a smoldering, reluctant, weary truce, which will burst into fresh fighting when the first hot coal touches an ever ready fuse.

The children in such a family, of course, have the idea that this is normal living, that life is such a continual series of fighting for some illusory personal advantage.

Johnny yells at Mary, "Gimme that or I'll knock your block off."

Mary yells back, "It's mine. It's mine."

Jane yells at both, "That is not yours. It's mine."

Then slaps and bangs all around.

Mother yells, "You kids cut that out this minute, or something is going to happen!"

Dad yells to mother, "If you'd hit once, instead of barking all the time, maybe you'd have a little discipline. They know you like I do. All they're afraid of is that you'll run off at the mouth a little more."

Mother yells, "Well, I sure don't get any help from you in disciplining this family. You help about as much around here as that hunting hound of yours that howls all night in the back yard."

The gloves are in the arena again. The bell rings. The battle is on once more for another Sunday afternoon.

It's a great life, a sad failure, a miserable way to live. In fact, it's a waste of living. No one benefits in family living of that kind. But a great many people have become habituated to selfish quarreling in a family. They lived it in their childhood family, they live it again in their own family. It never occurs to them that it is an unnecessary, undesirable state of affairs, that the family can be the center of something far better than that. They are surprised on being told that a family is possible without the least bickering and quarreling, in which everyone actually enjoys everyone else.

They reply, "You have to have a certain amount of quarreling and fighting, don't you?"

The picture of the unselfish family. What a vastly different sort of thing the family becomes when each of its members has developed the maturity of a feeling for other people, a genuine interest in them, a desire to make their days as pleasant and as meaningful an experience as possible. Basically, of course, this attitude benefits oneself, but here in the family the basic maturity of being unselfish easily matures to the point where interest in the welfare of the other people in the family becomes richly philanthropic and unattached to any strings of doing it for oneself, even though it still works for one's own good.

The best and simplest description of such a family was epitomized by a girl who was unfortunate enough to be born into a family of selfish, egocentric people. After several days visit at the home of a college girl friend she said, "This sure is a FUN family. You are having fun, like a circus, all the time."

That's exactly the atmosphere.

Such families enjoy living because each one finds it a joy to be pleasing everyone else.

Syrupy, oversweet, pollyannish, unreal?

Certainly not. Good, brisk, happy living, as thoroughly stimulating (though in a better direction) as a good fight.

In the odd moments at his work father is quietly thinking of something everyone would enjoy Saturday or Sunday afternoon. At dinner he suggests, "How would you nice people like to go to Reuben's Cave tomorrow afternoon?"

"Oh, good, Dad," Johnny says, "Can I take my bow and arrow?"

"Of course, you can. That would be a swell place to practice, no cows, no people, no windows to break."

"How about the canoe, Dad?" Jane asks.

"Yep, we'll take the canoe. In fact, we can't get to Reuben's Cave without the canoe."

"I'm going to take my camera," says Mary. "There are some lovely pictures up the river."

And mother comes into the picture. "I've got a new idea for a swell picnic lunch that will positively wow you."

And the scene is set for a really good time. No quarreling but everyone willing and anxious to add to everyone's enjoyment.

Mother, too, contributes mightily and adds to the family enterprise. She is always finding a rollicking book like "The Loud Red Patrick" or a thriller like "Little Axe Trowbridge" for the family to read in a circle after the evening meal. The evenings are spent helping the children with their school work or in playing games, or making things, or perhaps it may be an evening when each quietly pursues his own course.

As the children grow older the family circle discusses current events and controversial subjects like politics and religion, and the merits or demerits of this, that, and the other thing. Often they talk with gusto and enthusiasm, taking sides, but never, never do they let it develop into malice or ill feeling. Someone always manages to end the discussion on a good note.

Cooperation and mutual consideration is the keynote.

"Bill," Dad says one evening when the family has finished reading from a good book. "I'm afraid we can't send you back to college for this fall semester. Business has been slow, although it's going to pick up again. I'd suggest you keep on with the job you've had this summer and then with what you'll earn, and with what we'll have, go back again the following semester."

Bill, if he belonged in the other kind of family, would probably burst out with, "Oh, darn, there's always something like that to put a crimp in things." But belonging to the family he does, and having been brought up as he has, his attitude is at once cooperative and helpful.

"Sure, dad, I like this job. And when I go back to school I know where I can work for my board and room. That would help a lot, wouldn't it?"

Living in a family rich with such attitudes is the finest experience children can have. The only finer experience comes to them later on when they fashion their own families on the same pattern. Providing, of course, they don't marry some egocentric, immature crown of thorns.

Its members carry their spirit beyond the family. The people fortunate enough to be living in such a family carry their cooperative maturity with them into the outside world, into their contracts with people outside the family, to the people associated with their work, to the people at the club, or in the church, or on the bus. The children carry their attitudes of cooperation and consideration to school. The other children love them because they are easy to get along with, and they're fun, not trouble like so many of the other kids. The teachers find them a joy in their classes.

The whole world blooms around such people. The world wants them, finds them valuable for doing any kind of job. The world likes them socially. The world accepts them gladly, for there is no commodity as valuable to society or to an employer as a cooperative, unselfish attitude in a person. These people leave no wake of animosity behind them. Their every effort adds to the common good. And best of all, the atmosphere they bring with them is one of enjoyment and pleasure at just being alive.

Mean, egocentric people are apt to be envious of them and misjudge the cause of their success. "Oh, they are just awfully lucky; they sure have it easy; they have everything they want." Of course they have everything they want, because they do not selfishly want everything for themselves. They have it easy because their attitude makes living easy. They are lucky to be the way they are, to have had the conditioning to maturity that they had. Many people unfortunately were never placed in the way of such conditioning.

The people fortunate enough to have been conditioned to this maturity, however, have everything, even if they are poor materially. The greatest wealth they have is in the pleasure of seeing the other person pleased and happy by what they can do or say. There is no wealth nor pleasure to equal it. It's a FUN life.

But it's infinitely more than that. It's the one way in this world for truly belonging, for being truly useful, for being truly valuable, in the only true sense of those terms.

● The "Pay-Off" of Selfish Egoism

The root of the matter is simply that the selfish, egocentric attitude does not pay off. It is not an effective attitude for handling adult life, but results in infinitely more trouble than good. It's pay-off is only emotional stress and unhappiness.

Because it is such an ineffective attitude for handling adult life, egoism produces our greatest troubles—whether it operates at the domestic level in a family, at the community level in a village, town, or city, or at the national or international levels. The boomerang in egoism is that the world is so constructed that what produces trouble for other people brings trouble to oneself; whatever brings good to other people benefits oneself; and finally, one never benefits oneself without at the same time benefiting others.

But there is more harm in egoism than that. Do not forget that the selfish, self-seeking person is a very lonesome individual. People instinctively dislike anyone who is only for himself, who is impressed by his own importance, cocksure of his every idea, and just generally and hugely satisfied with himself.

But the final pay-off in egotistical selfish people and one which the doctor sees so frequently, is a reactive depression when they reach their 50's or 60's, or sometimes earlier. A reactive depression is only slightly less miserable than what is utterly the most miserable point in human life—the point at which a person is ready to commit suicide.

It comes about in this way: about the only solace possible to a selfish egoist is the degree of smug self-satisfaction it affords. But this balloon undergoes a deflation when the terrible truth begins to dawn on such a person that the household god he has set up (himself) is a phony; the qualities his self-conceit thought so remarkable turn out to be mediocre and nothing of great value. The bottom, all the ego-supported structure, drops out of his world. There is nothing left, it is all gone, the great ego has dissolved, there is no place to build a new concept or new hope. He wrings his hands, "I'm no good. All I've done is wrong." His egocentric attitude still remains in what is left of his thinking, "Oh! I'm no good and there is nothing else that is any good either. Life is futile; what's the use of it; everything is so futile; it's all no good."

That is the final, the not infrequent, pay-off.

It is so much easier, so much more effective, so much pleas-
anter, to live maturely with enlightened selfishness. And it is
not hard to do, especially for a woman, once you get the idea.

I. GIVING RATHER THAN RECEIVING

Another aspect of enlightened selfishness is that there is
nothing that adds more joy to your living than making a hobby
of *giving yourself, particularly where it isn't expected.* It is
the hobby of collecing glows and after-glows. Conducting life
on the basis of giving rather than receiving is one of the most
enlightened aspects of enlightened selfishness.

Next to having a predictably pleasant disposition there is
nothing that increases the basic pleasure of living as much as
giving yourself. It raises the level of good will and amity of
the circle in which we live. It gives one the personal satisfaction of being a help to humanity rather than a parasite. But
its greatest pleasure comes from seeing someone else pleased
and joyous.

Giving does not imply that we should want only to give away
our substance and leave ourselves stranded without adequate
food and shelter, or without savings against the time of our old
age. That would be foolish and ridiculously immature; it would
be detrimental to our interests rather than beneficial.

Give yourself. The commodities all of us can give freely are
appreciation, loyalty, understanding, kindness, interest, encouragement, tolerance, pleasant moments, a bit of humor, inspiration, and many little joys.

Be sure to give yourself without any strings attached or
you'll take the most important pleasure out of it.

In his delightful little book, *Try Giving Yourself Away,* David
Dunn tells how he made a hobby of giving himself away.[1] He
gives such examples as these:

> One spring evening I stopped at a popcorn wagon
> in Battle Creek, Michigan. A couple of urchins
> watched hungrily as the melted butter was poured

[1] The Updegraff Press, Inc.: Scarsdale, N. Y., 1947.

on the freshly popped corn. Without seeming to notice the youngsters, I ordered two more bags, paid for them, handed each of the boys his bag, and strode away. This little adventure-in-giving made the world more exciting for four people that evening—for the popcorn vendor, too, enjoyed the episode.

And this,

One evening I was dining alone in a Boston hotel. The selections the orchestra was playing exactly suited my mood. On the way out, impulse prompted me to cross the dining room to the dais where the musicians were resting between numbers.

"Gentlemen," I said, "I have thoroughly enjoyed your program. Several of your numbers were particular favorites of mine. And you put so much spirit into your playing, I want to thank you."

Their faces broke into smiles, and I left them beaming over their instruments. The rest of my own evening was happier.

And this,

On Saturday afternoon while working in my garden I thought of an idea which I believed a certain New York department store might find useful. That evening I wrote a letter to the store outlining the idea and presenting it, as is my custom, "with no strings attached." It was adopted with appreciation—and I had acquired a big department store as a friend.

The average mother has an excellent start in giving herself away. Her attitude toward her children is not, "What are these children doing for me?" but, "What can I do for them?"

But too many women do not capitalize on the same principle of giving in their contacts with people outside the family. There they need to cultivate the art of giving themselves just as much as men do.

● *Childhood Conditioning in Giving and Receiving*

As we have seen, the conditions of childhood are natural conditioners for a selfish attitude of receiving, and many people grow to adulthood without ever changing in this.

But there is an age in youngsters, between five and seven, when they begin to sense the joys of giving, and a bit of help from the parents can swing them toward the mature attitude of giving.

Has it ever been your pleasure to watch a child who has given something he or she made to someone else as a Christmas present?

You have admired their face, wide-eyed with expectant glee, and a body vibrant with a high pitch of anticipation. And when the present they are giving is opened and the recipient expresses astonishment and gives superlative compliments on the fine quality and usefulness of the gift, the child fairly glows with delight, and is pleased, tremendously and powerfully pleased, inside.

The joy and pleasure they show with this kind of giving appears to exceed the pleasure they show as they open their own gifts around the Chirstmas tree. This they enjoy, too, but often with an air of mercenary assurance that they had it coming, which detracts a great deal from their own enjoyment, and certainly lowers the spirit of the meeting as far as the parents are concerned.

It would appear that even the fairly young child gets more pleasure out of giving, too, but he hasn't awakened to the fact yet. He needs to be encouraged to indulge in it more often so as to get its true feel, and to appreciate that he feels better when he gives than when he receives.

One thing that very definitely elevates the flow of pleasure in giving, is having created the gift oneself, the feeling that we are giving *something of ourselves,* whether it be an object we have made, or a kindly deed. Giving of *oneself* seems to provide an important element in raising the degree of resulting pleasure. The pleasure of giving a handbag made with one's own hands far exceeds the pleasure of giving a purchased bag.

This additional element of pleasure probably consists in having one's creative talents recognized and praised; it amounts to a cultivation and fertilization of one's ego. Granted that this is true. However, although the pleasure in giving the created gift is an indication of a kind of selfishness, it is very

definitely the desirable variety of selfishness which we have
called "enlightened selfishness."

But even in giving the created gift, there is certainly in the
mature adult a large amount of pleasure coming, not from the
praise received, but from knowing the other is benefitted or
pleased—a genuine outgoing feeling without any of the over-
tones of a looked-for return.

A generous, giving lady in our town. Such was the lady
in our town, a lady of generous proportions, generous in giving
her time and services to anyone needing them or not. All summer this lady sat on a chair in front of her little shop, con-
tributing a witty pleasantry to every passer-by. Her winter, too,
was spent in the front of her little store and restaurant, sitting
behind the large front window, scraping any ice off to keep a
clear view of the world outside.

The children of the village knew that in summer they had
only to stand and gaze wistfully for a moment at the open
boxes of fruit, displayed outside the store, and they would be
rewarded with a plum or cherry by the generous lady. If
some enterprising young embryo-racketeer developed this into
a system, she would say quite seriously, after about the sixth
visit, with the twinkle never leaving her eye:

"Now, Sonny, we can't be doing this all the time; we have
to leave some, you know, for other people."

If someone in the village was sick and without adequate
help, she locked the shop for an hour and went to make them
comfortable and to tidy up their house.

The meals she carried to the sick, old, and poor through the
years must have numbered in the high hundreds. And hardly
a day went by but she penned a greeting to someone with a
birthday or an anniversary of some kind that they themselves
might have forgotten about. The village mayor, whoever he
might be, always received her congratulations and commendations on each anniversary of his taking office. It was usually
the only pat on the back he received during his entire tenure.
A bouquet of flowers on the church altar every Sunday was a
regular and unconsidered habit, as were the boxes that went
regularly (not only at Christmas) and quietly and without

fanfare to several poor families in the neighborhood. Twice a
year, in the little restaurant she kept in the back of her store,
she served a banquet meal to the schoolteachers, who in those
days were all single girls away from home. Her restaurant
meals were served, depending on who was the recipent, at little
or no cost.

And so she lived, alone but not lonesome, finding her pleasure in being good, kindly, and of help to everyone. She never
gave evidence (and I knew her well) of doing it to receive
the praise of others.

Let us come back to the matter of the *enlightened selfishness*
that resides in giving.

Besides his personal pleasures, the person who gives *does*
benefit a great deal from a different sort of thing—the good
will toward himself he provokes in other people and which
provides his life with a warm atmosphere and with the rain-
bowed aura of other people's regard.

The crabbed, snooping critic can quite properly label this
a form of selfishness. It is, but again of the approved, enlightened, and permissible variety.

People, practically *all* people, except the misanthrope, naturally like an out-going person like the generous lady in our
town. And conversely, everyone develops a dislike for the
habitually in-taking person.

The lady who never gave. Our town had a rich lady who
lived, as all such people seem to live, in the big house on top
of the hill. Although she never did any actual harm or injury
to anyone, she never did any good either. Without exception
the townspeople disliked her. A mother would say to a naughty
child. "Just you behave, or I'll call Mrs. ——!"

Her glance at children passing her house on the way to
school, which was also on the hill, was as much as to say,
"Don't you dare come in here." She looked at them *under* her
glasses — down her nose, so to speak — which is an indication of
unkindliness, rather than *over* her glasses, which is a sign of
kindliness.

Her reputation was summed up in two stories the villagers

loved to relate about the two times she had ever been known to laugh.

The first time she was known to have laughed, or at least cackled, was the time she was solicited by a representative of the Ladies Aid to contribute to a fund for buying Mrs. Regula Altman an artificial leg. Regula had lost her leg many years before and through the years had bumped along on a hard wooden peg.

"Doesn't she have a leg?" the lady asked.

"Only a wooden peg," the solicitor answered.

"Well, hasn't she been getting around on that?"

"Yes, but a good artificial leg would be a wonderful help to her."

"Well, if her family had saved their money as they should have, they could buy her a leg. I'm saving mine so I can buy my own leg if I ever need one. Goodbye."

As the door closed behind the solicitor, she heard a laugh— a cackle, she said, like a hen that had just laid an egg.

The second time occurred one slippery winter day.

Old man Bot Elmer's crochety old horse was panting and frantic, slipping and sliding, trying to pull a loaded wagon up the icy hill near the lady's home. Old Bot was walking on the ice beside his horse, urging and pushing it so hard he was panting too, and blue in the face. Finally the horse made one last valiant effort and fell down dead, breaking the wagon shaft and falling on top of Old Bot, breaking his arm and leg too. Pinned under the weight of the animal, Bot called loudly for help. The lady of the house on the hill came to her gate, so the story goes, more out of curiosity than to offer help.

Seeing her standing at her gate, Bot called, "Get me out, oh, get me out."

"What do you want me to do?" she yelled without going over. "Lift off the horse? Pull yourself out!"

And Bot said she laughed. He said she cackled like a hen that had just laid an egg.

Every person holds the choice of living with a receiving attitude or with a giving attitude. If you are hard to persuade that giving is the better of the two, try them both. If you find that grabbing and wanting and getting gives *you* more pleasure, then by all means make it the attitude of your life.

And you need not fear, when you are old and soured and alone in an old house, rattling in a lonely bed with a bad cold that looks like the last thing you'll ever receive, don't worry. Some generous neighbor, like the lady of the little store, will bring in some soup and tidy you up before long.

It's nice to have people like her in the world.

II. CHEATING NO ONE AND STEALING NOTHING

Honesty is one of the oldest virtues, and it has always been a popular one. In most general textbooks of psychology and psychiatry, honesty is usually classed as a maturity in its own right. And indeed a person can aspire to be honest merely because it is easier to stay out of trouble than to get out of it once you are in it.

But honesty is really a part of the maturity of being able to identify oneself with others in considerate understanding and enlightened selfishness. In fact honesty becomes most dependable and richly defined when it is built on that basis. Dishonesty and cheating of course harm us, but they harm others as well, and a person mature in his consideration for others will indulge in neither.

A mother must instil honesty into her children, as well as be strictly honest herself; she cannot successfully teach honesty if she is not a paradigm of honesty herself.

Any family in which dishonesty is taught by inference and by example is a failure of the most flagrant type. The family may teach its children no other maturity; it may be an influence, as many families are, for developing grossly immature young adults, but at least it must teach honesty. That is the very least that can be expected of any family. Society has no place for young adults who are dishonest and who cheat, except possibly a jail. Such people are forever fugitives and outlaws in society.

It is almost impossible to raise an honest child who remains immature in most other respects, since honesty is linked to other maturities, especially to the maturity of consideration and understanding of others. The child thief, or the teen-age thief, or the adult thief, takes things because he *wants* selfishly; he destroys or steals the property of others because he cannot identify himself with them in any sort of considerate understanding.

Gross immaturity in essential fields usually means immaturity in most other ways, including dishonesty.

A mother, if she is to raise children who are dependable and honest, must also provide them with an abundance of maturity in other fields of living.

That is just one other of the capacities required of the successful woman.

6

Living with Confidence
Instead of Fear

Maturity No. 4

● Fear Is Universal in Human Beings

The difference between a brave man and a coward is that the brave man admits his fear, the coward denies it. Everyone is capable of fear.

Violent fear is one of man's most horrible experiences.

Some of the most pitiful humans are those who never grow out of a childhood state of fear and spend their lives pursued by a host of immature fears.

Children and immature adults have vague, unfounded fears. The more mature a person becomes, the fewer fears he has of the vague variety, and the more confidently he meets the truly threatening situation.

Paradoxical fear in the "fearless" he-man variety of the species. There is an interesting and fairly common specimen of the male human who grows up under the delusion that maturity consists of being a fearless "he-man," with a surly disregard of any values other than his own. A typical example of the latter type was a St. Louis gangster who achieved national notoriety in the Prohibition days of the 1920's.

This fellow had persuaded himself that he was absolutely fearless. To prove it he took up the vocation of machine-gun-

108

ning beer trucks through the police network, and as a lucrative and exciting side line he kidnapped wealthy citizens. He was the typical "tough-as-they-come" hoodlum, with a cigarette drooping from the left side of his mouth while the right side derisively muttered, "Oh, yeah?" just as his trigger finger drilled a hole through someone he didn't like.

Unfortunately he picked up syphilis in the course of his career and needed medical attention. This "fearless" gunman would literally go into a panic of fear whenever a doctor or nurse was about to give him a hypodermic injection. He would plead, perspire, tremble, and defend himself against the needle like a four-year-old child. The injection could finally be given only by shaming him with the reminder of what his circle of similarly fearless toughs would think if they witnessed his act. Later, when he was out of medical care, he tried unsuccessfully to "liquidate" the doctor. He could not bear to have anyone alive know what a coward he really was. Fellows like this, secretly ashamed of their strong fears, assume their role of tough as a defense mechanism.

Fears may be justified, or vague and unjustified. Anyone can be expected to feel fear when he is face-to-face with an alarming threat of harm; anyone is justifiably anxious when possible harm sits on the horizon. Such fear and anxiety is natural and unavoidable.

But it is neither natural nor desirable to have a fear state or an anxiety state when there is nothing substantial to be afraid of or to be anxious about. Some people have abnormal, unreasonable fears and anxieties on very slight provocation, or what often seems to outsiders no provocation at all. Their fears and anxieties are composed of the filmy mist of fantasy. Yet their fears are none the less real for all that; in fact, they are more disabling because they pop up so easily on such small pretext. Pity rather than belittle such anxiety-ridden people, for their lives are a series of unbelievably miserable days. They are as severely crippled as if they lacked an extremity or two.

Horrible episodes may condition fears. Some of these ungrounded and peculiar fears are conditioned by terrifying experiences early in life. These experiences may leave a scar on the personality for the rest of one's life.

For instance, when Albert was five years old, he was riding on a wagon through a storm with his father. A single bolt of lightning killed his father and the two horses, leaving him at first stunned, then terrified and alone in the storm with death all around him. Later in life he would go into virtual panic at the sight of black clouds or lightning, or on hearing thunder. The rattle of a wagon or the sound of horses' hoofs made him acutely uncomfortable.

In her childhood Jane was stranded alone between floors in an automatic elevator; rescue was a long time coming and she became frantic with terror. Today she becomes panicky to the point of collapse if she tries to ride an elevator alone. She experiences the same panic if she enters a red room, because the color of the original elevator was red.

A Marine lived through the landing on Iwo Jima; he survived the constant machine gunning, the incessant pounding of heavy artillery, with his buddies dying and blown to bits on all sides of him. Later in life a loud bang of any kind near him made him shake, perspire, and feel faint. This boy had received the highest decoration for bravery in action. Brave men are not without fear, and are conditioned to fear like anyone else.

Some of our fear conditioning is the result of single, terrifying episodes like the above, but most fear conditioning, and especially anxiety conditioning, is due to the immature ways in which parents bring up children.

Fears are not necessary in children. The child is born with but three or four innate fears: fear of sudden loud and shrill noises, fear of falling, fear upon sudden arousal from sleep, and fear upon being held too tightly. The child has to be conditioned to be afraid of the dark, to be anxious about someone being under the bed, to be hysterically afraid of snakes, to be afraid of being away from mother, or the many other fears considered "normal" in children.

A fear can be very easily conditioned in a child because the child is so basically ignorant of the great wide world. Seen through the eyes of the child, the world and human existence are vast unexplored tracts that have not been reduced to understanding.

Suggested fantasy holds as much weight with a child, if not more, than actual fact. It is easy for a child to picture the unknown as threatening, to populate it with demons, especially when the vociferous adults around it refer to those *awful* Russians and the *wicked* English, and those *terrible* Democrats or Republicans. It takes nothing more than adult suggestion, often inadvertent suggestion, to get a child to read into the world a preponderance of bad over good, of evil purpose prevailing over good purpose, of wicked forces confusing and routing the good forces.

Most anxiety states in adults have the same nebulous quality of a vague apprehension about an indefinite something or other that characterizes anxiety in children. Things well understood rarely cause anxiety and fear. Fear and anxiety breed on incomplete and partial knowledge; the more incomplete and partial the greater the fear.

Parents are the most potent force for conditioning fear and anxiety in the child. An anxious, apprehensive mother provides an example that sets the pattern for the children. Her reaction to things is considered by young children as the norm. A mother always worrying about a pain here and there gets her children to worrying about similar pains.

"Oh, dear, isn't that mean old bottle giving you any milk?"; "Darling! Are you SURE you didn't hurt yourself?"; "Don't go near that horrible fan"; "Be careful of strangers, and come right home." It isn't so much *what* is said as *how* it is said, what intonations of exaggerated emotion the voice portrays.

A father may be an ameliorating influence to such an anxious mother, and if he has a kindly understanding, he may soften an overly-anxious wife's apprehension and teach the children a truer attitude. But all too often he too helps condition a chronic anxiety state in children, especially if he has a harsh and mean outlook or is savage in his disciplining.

A stern, harsh father or mother, constantly threatening and reprimanding, conditions not only fear in the child but resentment and rejection, often to such an extent that the child goes through life with an injustice complex and a chip on his shoulder.

A divorce is a family calamity whose bad effects a child seldom completely outgrows. The fact that two people as basic in the child's world as father and mother cannot get along with each other, conditions the child to major uncertainty about the stability and durability of anything in the world. They anxiously expect life to be insecure, and the expectation is a help in making it so. It is easy to see why the children of divorced parents are themselves so frequently divorced.

Sex is a common source of anxiety. Any part of life surrounded with the mystery of ignorance and the prohibition of strong tabus is an excellent subject for anxiety conditioning. Nothing fulfills these requirements as completely as does sex. The initial impulse of the child to handle or inspect its genitalia, an entirely natural act, is met with stern and (to the child) seemingly unreasonable reprimands. All during childhood and adolescence sex remains number one among the unmentionables, treated as something loaded to the gunwales with sin, all the more terrible for being vague, and all the more vague for being kept so veiled.

● **The Mature Attitude, Confident Living, Is Developed in the Family**

The mature attitude recognizes, first, that certain true dangers exist in ordinary living — such as ill health, auto accidents, fire, and so on — and then takes a reasonable precaution to avoid them.

Beyond such sensible precautions, the person with the mature attitude is confident that he will be able to deal satisfactorily with whatever life brings, that he will be able to make living go well.

Instiling this mature attitude in children is one of the essential duties of parenthood. Parents who can't give it to their children are failing in a very important way.

Children are best taught this maturity by the example of mother and father living courageously and confidently without constantly whining about difficulties. The family should avoid howling about calamities and making predictions of ill fortune and disaster. At no time should the family allow griping about events and people. Unfortunate events and wayward people should always be discussed in a factual and *constructive* way — sympathetic, understanding, and helpful in orientation — rather than in a way that is derogatory, critical or ill-willed.

The parental attitude toward children should not be a constant, everlasting haranguing and warning about alarming dangers. One can do a tremendous amount of harm to the developing child by saying, "Now you just be good, or I'll call the ogre that punishes bad little boys." Similarly, it is bad to have an attitude in the family of "Be careful at those street crossings, or you'll be hit by a car and killed or crippled for life."

How much better to create the atmosphere that security, safety, and confidence belong to those who live sensibly and reasonably. "I know you are sensible and careful. If you always look both ways and think of what you are doing, you will have no trouble."

The family should arise each morning with the cheerful attitude that it is going to be a grand day, that it is *good* to be alive. *Family* attention should be kept on the good things in living, on the bright side to every event, and on the good in people. The attitude should always be:

"Of course there is nothing to worry about unless we let ourselves worry."

Such an attitude is possible in a family only if mother and father have it themselves. Children just naturally pick it up through contact and make it a part of themselves just as they pick up the opposite attitude of fear from their parents.

The parents should stay alert to the moment when the child becomes alarmed and develops fear. At that moment a calm, reassuring discussion of the matter will dispel the possibility of searing an indelible scar into the child's personality. This discussion should be one of realistic appraisal.

Let us suppose the child learns that a robber entered a neighbor's house and shot the neighbor when he tried to resist. The child's world suddenly becomes insecure. He readily assumes that such crimes are common, and something similar will certainly happen at home. The wise parent will notice the child's concern and will meet it with the explanation that such events are very uncommon in our well-regulated world, and happen only very infrequently when some pitiful individual, because of constant defeat in his life, makes the serious mistake of committing a robbery or some other crime; the owner of the house would certainly have done better not to have opposed the armed bandit. The bandit is hurting no one as much as himself. He will probably be caught; but even if he is not, he will have to live with the uncomfortable and everlasting thought of the harm he has done to someone else; he will find that what he has stolen will give him only the uneasy feeling of being a thief, a rascal, and a failure. The parents' own obvious lack of fear of robbers in their own home will go a long way to give the child an attitude of courage rather than fear.

One of the best ways of developing maturity in the family is in group readings around the table and in the living room. The parents will find ample opportunity to comment on events or on something that is said, or something that is read, in such a way as to plant the idea that simple courage is a human virtue and a personal asset, that an attitude of fear is unnecessary and is born of fantasy and partial knowledge.

● Avoiding Fear of Death

It is especially important that parents give the child a wholesome courage and view of death. So many people grow up with an avid fear of death. Death, of course, is as much an expected and necessary part of living as is being born, and is to be regarded as a natural event, if not exactly entirely welcome, at least acceptable and not in the least frightening. Too often an unwarranted fear of death and dying is started through some silly, thoughtless remarks of a parent.

As a physician, I have always been impressed with the easy

satisfaction with which most people die, and of how at the moment of passing from life to death their faces assume the calm of a profound peace. There is nothing in the least bad about dying. As Socrates remarked in his "Apology," it is passing into a deep sleep (and what is easier than a deep sleep) or into another life controlled by a Supreme Power whose motivations, you may be sure, are far superior and far finer than any motivations mere human beings have ever achieved or ever imagined.

Some prefer the idea of peaceful sleep; to others the idea of eternity is appealing.

The wise parent will refer to death as a natural event one meets with calm and confidence.

● Ours Is a Fear Economy

It is very important, then, that by the time one reaches adulthood and begins earning a living, one has developed the maturity of living courageously and without fear. If one has not, life will become a continual anxiety, an anxiety fed, among other things, by our economic system.

As humanity grows older and people become more mature, a society may be developed that will provide such a degree of security for the individual that fear will become a forgotten emotion. Such is far from the case now. Every economic and social order thus far evolved by man has been a conditioner of fear. Our present economic system is no exception. It is really very immature and loaded with uncertainties and hazards of many varieties, not the least of which is the uncertainty provided by highly competitive methods at all levels, and another is the uncertainty of the system itself. Even when times are good, people must fear an economic depression or they must fear inflation. Savings or annuities laid aside in youth may be worthless by the time one has reached retirement. Everywhere men, women, and children are afraid. Tests in ten-year-old children recently showed that a common fear in the ten-year-old group is that of the father losing his job. Not only the children, but the wives and the husbands themselves are afraid for their jobs. Others fear that they may not get their expected advancement. Others are afraid of being laid on the shelf and of not getting another job in middle life. Others are afraid they may not get the top job they have had their eyes on. Small business men are afraid their businesses will break beneath big chain store competition. Big business fears a bigger or a smarter business may force it to the wall. Salesmen fear they may not reach their sales goal. Workmen on the line fear they may not turn out their quota of pieces. Manufacturers fear that public demand for their goods may drop or be diverted to a more appealing product made by a competitor.

Ours is a fear economy, a throwback to the age-old idea that fear is a prime incentive. Unless a person in his youth reaches the maturity of living courageously and without fear, it will be difficult for him to acquire it later when all these fear-conditioning elements in our society begin to influence him.

● *How to Get Over Your Fears*

Fortunate is the person who has graduated from the immaturity of unreasonable and unfounded fear.

But what of the person who was not so fortunate in his early conditioning, and who, in his adult life, is made miserable by a recurring fear or anxiety state? What is he or she to do? Can his fear be deconditioned? Can he be freed from the miserable shackles that hold him?

Yes, he can. There is much that can be done to *decondition* oneself to severe fears and anxieties that are crippling one's life.

To get rid of a fear it is necessary:

(1) *to see exactly what is feared, and,*
(2) *to see exactly what the fear is.*

The two are quite different, and one needs to know exactly what each is.

1. Find out exactly what is feared. First assess and analyze the *thing* that is feared. Take it apart, look at it piece by piece; learn *all* there is to know about the thing feared, see what a sham and a joker it really is.

Grace, aged 28, was morbidly afraid of getting multiple sclerosis. She thought it was a bacterial or virus disease and could be acquired through contact. Consequently she was continually scrubbing her hands and her house; constantly waging a year-around battle to keep everything fumigated and free of germs and trying to stay away from people she thought had contacted someone having multiple sclerosis.

She was surprised to learn that multiple sclerosis is not due to a germ and that it is not transmitted from one person to another. She was surprised to learn that multiple sclerosis can be a regressive disease as well as a progressive one; that is, that one can completely recover from it. She was surprised to learn many other things about it.

However, knowing all these fundamental things about the thing feared, and seeing that her fear was entirely unfounded, did not rid her of the fear. She went right on with the compulsion of washing herself and her house, and avoiding certain people. She needed to know, in addition, "why is it feared."

Nevertheless, analyzing exactly what is feared is a necessary first step.

2. *Understand why it is feared.* Next—understand *the fear itself.*

How did the fear begin?

What were the conditions and the situations that brought the fear on? And most important of all, *what is the mechanism that keeps it going?*

● How Did the Fear Begin?

The start of most fears and anxieties is obvious enough. Most of them are the result of family influences, such as a nervous, over-anxious, complaining mother, or a terror-producing, stern father. These are the common influences that initiate most anxiety states.

Or the fear may have started with a single episode. A boy riding through a storm has both horses and his father killed by a bolt of lightning. A girl is caught alone between floors in a red elevator.

Grace was tired and feeling badly when she went to a church supper and sat opposite a person who had severe multiple sclerosis and had much trouble eating and moving about. She had never seen anyone like this before. The person with multiple sclerosis spilled food on his clothes, and upset a dish of spaghetti passed to him. Grace helped clean up the poor fellow after each catastrophe. Then she herself dropped a piece of buttered bread on her clean skirt, tipped over a glass of milk, and upset her chair when she got up. The fear flashed into her tired mind that she herself was developing multiple sclerosis.

After that she could never bring herself to go back to that church harboring the person with multiple sclerosis, nor could she associate with any of the "contaminated" people belonging to that church, not even her father and mother who had sat next to the sick man.

There is a school of "Go Back and Dig it Up" psychiatrists who believe that a fear or anxiety is not a conditioned state, but is a defensive mechanism whose purpose is to hide from the ego the fact that some *intolerable* repressed impulse of the *id* is trying to get out into the open. And Grace spent hourly sessions for many years on a psychiatrist's couch free-wheeling back through the years.

Very little is ordinarily accomplished by this method of "Go Back and Dig it Up." All that usually has happened by the time the repressed impulse is "found" is a new fear of one's inner stability—the fear of losing one's mind. As a method of therapy it is one of the most disappointing developments of our century.

But knowing that the fear started in a certain way and under certain conditions is necessary in establishing an exact knowledge in the mind of the person of exactly what is feared. This is necessary for the next step, knowing exactly what the fear is.

The mechanism that keeps the fear going. The fear itself —the awful, panicky feeling of impending disaster that Grace gets when she sees someone from her church, or the thought that people coming into her home are bringing in multiple sclerosis—consists of a pounding heart, trembling hands, a difficulty in breathing, a light head, and weak legs.

The fear itself is a PHYSICAL STATE that has been cross-conditioned to many things.

The emotion of fear is a physical experience, just as all emotions, good or bad, are entirely physical. The emotion of fear consists of violent physical and chemical changes in the body. The heart pounds wildly as if about to part its moorings; the blood pressure climbs like a rocket only to come down later just about as fast into a state of shock; small muscles in the skin literally make the hair stand on end; this together with an extensive crop of goose pimples produce that eery, shrinking feeling that goes with fear; cold sweat pours over the body adding another increment of discomfort; the breath comes short and with difficulty, the air one breathes has a terrifying way of not wanting to get to the bottom of the lungs; all the intestinal organs seem to quake and feel as if they were engaging in a St. Vitus dance; the stomach seems to be sinking into a bottomless abyss, the heart alternately chokes the throat and dives off a precipice; the intestines begin to convulse and there may be an involuntary defecation or micturition; the legs feel miserably weak as though unable to carry one, and indeed they may buckle under the attempt; the head is a mixture of confusion, pressure, and giddiness, then faintness, possibly followed by a complete blackout and unconsciousness. These physical changes *are* the emotion of fear. They are what fear consists of.

These physical changes which *are* fear are switched on automatically when Grace contacts anyone of a number of conditioning factors. The physical state of fear is switched on the moment Grace sees a member of that church, or if she thinks about the contamination of her own hands.

Whenever Grace sees a member of her church in the store in which she works, cold clammy fear seizes her, without her thinking about multiple sclerosis. She must run to the wash room and "wash her hands of germs."

An anxiety may be conditioned and brought on by a certain

room, a certain place, a certain object, a certain circumstance, or a certain train of thinking.

In other words, the fear or anxiety, once established as a conditioned physical event, is no longer a notion, it is an emotion. You can talk yourself out of a notion, but you can't talk yourself out of the emotion. That cannot be dispelled by analyzing the fear and reasoning that the substance of the fear is flimsy stuff.

But it can be deconditioned.

It can be deconditioned by the following steps:

1. Realize that the physical symptoms (which *are* the emotion of fear or anxiety) switch on automatically whenever the switch is tripped by any one of many conditioning factors.

2. Tell yourself constantly not to be afraid of the symptoms of the emotion—the pounding heart, the trembling limbs, the difficult breathing—all these things are nothing bad, nothing serious, nothing harmful but are merely the manifestations of a conditioned emotion.

3. Deliberately expose yourself to the conditioning factor to bring on the fear; go into a crowd, go into the church, go into the elevator, go into the red room, stay at home alone, whatever it is, and tell yourself repeatedly in a *triumphant*, determined way, "I'm going to lick this thing." Then deliberately repeat and repeat the exposure, maintaining the same triumphant and determined attitude. The feeling of courage grows each time the fear is successfully lived through. Each time the fear is lived through the fear grows weaker, the courage stronger.

In this way a fear or anxiety can be deconditioned.

Jane went up and down an elevator alone 78 times in one week telling herself not to give in to her feeling of panic, repeating to herself with triumphant determination, "I'm going to lick this thing," at first with fierce resolution, then with a growing gladness at her obvious triumph.

Grace, too, gradually deconditioned herself out of needless washings of hands and staying away from contaminated people.

The immaturities of fear and anxiety fill the lives of countless people with stark, painful misery of the very worst kind.

An excellent conditioning against the possibility of being conditioned to a fear is to develop, as early as possible in life, and to keep developing it as one grows older, the mature attitude in Walt Whitman's two lines in his *Leaves of Grass:*

And I will show that whatever happens to anybody
may be turned to beautiful results,
And I will show that nothing can happen more
beautiful than death.

7

It Is Unnecessary to Be
Irritated or Angry

Maturity No. 5

You are not that way yourself, of course, but have you ever had to live, even a day, with someone who was forever peeved and irritated, quickly belligerent, and angry over every little trifle?

A belief has persisted that ready anger or general aggressiveness is the sign of a strong adult personality. Far from it! It is a childish attitude that accomplishes nothing and ruins a person's entire life. Anything like enjoyable living is impossible for someone who is constantly finding fault and getting angry.

There are degrees of anger varying all the way from peeved irritation and cutting remarks to full-blown, volcanic eruptions of rage.

Ordinarily we think of a person being peeved and irritated by some *trifle,* and angry over something of *major magnitude.* But such is not the case. Immature people disposed to irritation and anger become enraged over trifles. A mature person, on the other hand, will be angered, if at all, only by a most flagrant offense to his sensibilities, and even then he will quickly rise above it with the proper perspective of maturity.

As people have grown more civilized (which is equivalent to saying more mature) degrading fits of anger among people have become less common, I believe. But there are still many

122

immature people who nurse a smoldering spark of anger that bursts into flame with the slightest stir of air.

Such a person is a nuisance and a trouble to himself. But he is ten times more of a nuisance and trouble to the person unfortunate enough to have to live with him. The only justice would be that a person with a volatile temper be mated with someone having an equally volatile temper. The life such a couple leads together is a fitting compensation to repay both for their tempers.

Two such well-mated people sat in my office one morning.

● Two Adults Who Became Enraged over Tremendous Trifles

The couple were in my office because of the wife's constant headaches, which concerned the husband merely because he was having to do more and more of the housework while the wife lay abed nursing her headache with ice packs.

The interview was not yet well started when the wife said to me, by way of making conversation:

"The weather looks as though we were going to have a storm."

Before I could answer the husband exploded:

"Oh, you're always looking for trouble!"

"I'm not either," her voice rising a degree or two, "You're the one who is always starting the trouble in this family."

"Is that so? Who started it this noon, when . . ."

And they were off; around and around they went.

I thought I would let them go to see how long their silly argument would last and what direction it would take. After five minutes they had battled back through the sordid details of a stormy morning, each unbeaten, unbowed, and more angry than ever. Next they went at each others' throats over an alleged breach of etiquette that one of them had perpetrated on the other at a bridge party the night before.

Many couples spend their entire lives in this sort of cantankerous atmosphere. What an utterly unnecessary and silly way to live! With less childishness in their make-ups they could just as easily get along smoothly. It requires nothing but the common sense of maturity to get along with other people.

It was well expressed by a great actress of our century who was giving a reception celebrating her 50th wedding anniversary. She was being interviewed by a young lady newspaper reporter who asked the great lady to disclose her secret for a happily married life.

The great actress replied simply, "My dear, just rise above it!"

● **One Might Expect Two Children to Fight Over Nothing**

These two childish adults were no different than the two four-year-old children I had watched the day before playing train with a set of plain, unmarked blocks.

One of them grabbed a block the other had, "This is *my* engine!"

"Aw, that ain't no engine. That's a caboose. I said it was a caboose."

" 'Tisn't neither. It's an engine."

"Aw, you don't know how to play!"

"I do so. It's you who doesn't know how to play!"

"If you're not going to play right, I won't play."

And with that he knocked the lines of cars, engines, and cabooses into chaos. Then the arguing really started, taking them into ridiculous phases of absurdity.

● **The Absurdity of Anger**

There is something amusing—amusing in much the same way that a man with a five o'clock beard masquerading as an infant is amusing—to see an adult lose control of his intelligence, his sanity, and himself, by flying into a volcanic eruption of anger, spitting vituperatives and pouring molten lava over everything. One feels sorry for him when his top is blown off and he sputters to a miserable half-apologetic stop, slinking away with his tail of human dignity between his legs.

Such a spectacle is amusing only to someone who is not caught in its path too often. Having to live with someone who constantly blows his top is one of humanity's most disagreeable ways of living.

Becoming angry is not a form of insanity although it has all the appearances. Anger is the persistence of an infantile reaction in an adult, and is not to be regarded, as it sometimes is, as the strength of a powerful personality. People prone to blowing their tops prefer to think of it as something other than immaturity, as a quality actually desirable and valuable in human beings. They are like the fox in Aesop's fable who accidentally lost his fine tail and then insisted that all other foxes should have their tails cut off.

● **The Sad Case of Jane and her Immature Reactions**

A housewife who begins letting trifles irritate her will forever lead a miserable life, for there is nothing as capable of producing peeves and irritations in a susceptible person as is bringing up a family.

Jane was a typical and pitiful example of a housewife given to petty irritations and anger.

Jane had always been upset by tremendous trifles. The influence of her childhood family was toward immaturity, mainly because of her mother who was always irritated or angry over something.

If Jane *ever* had it, and I doubt it, she had long ago lost any enthusiasm for meeting another day. Getting breakfast was a sour-faced, sombre march from the ice box to the stove with eggs she was sure were not as fresh as the grocer said, to the table with butter that wasn't the grade A the creamery stamped it, from the bread box to the table with bread that was poorly baked (what kind of bakers were there nowadays?).

Breakfast she turned into another dead loss. Her conversation was never on a happy, pleasant level. In it there was always the eternal note of irritation at tremendous trifles.

"George, you're terrible. You never do anything for me I ask you to do. Did you remember today and stop at the hardware store and get a catch for the screen door? You never remember a thing."

"Mary, I don't want you to have a thing to do with that Rodke boy; he just isn't the type."

"Johnny, if you don't bring home all that dirty stuff in your locker at school, you're going right back for it."

Whatever possibility there might have been to make breakfast the start of an enjoyable day, was killed by Jane's irritation over trifles, her anger over nothing.

To Jane shopping was an irritating chore like everything else. Shopping provided her with a *real* opportunity for getting all upset. The stores were crowded; she hated crowds. The clerks were busy; she hated busy clerks. In fact, she hated clerks. Most of the time she hated herself.

"Well! I guess the clerk doesn't want to wait on me! All right, I'll go somewhere else."

But somewhere else was no different because Jane was no different. The frazzled clerks treated her with the same attitude she showed them, and both Jane and the clerks became irritated. Jane invariably found fault with the merchandise, whatever it might be. If there was nothing else wrong, the prices were too high.

Her lunch in a department store restaurant was another complete immersion in trivial irritations. She was aggravated at having to wait for a table; she was disgusted because the menu didn't have what she wanted (no menu would have been any better); she was dismayed because the service was slow; sullen because the waitress was sullen; irritated because nothing was prepared well — it was all poorly seasoned, poorly selected, poorly served. The noise drove her into a frenzy, the size of the check outraged her, and the way the cashier slid the change across the counter instead of putting it into her outstretched hand—well, it called for a nasty, sharp, and unnecessary remark.

Jane took her absorption with trifles to bed with her at night. What should have been a night's rest became an "I can see it now" program in which her mind regretfully reviewed the tremendous trifles of the preceding day. That review having been completed and reviewed several times, she indulged in an anticipatory review of the next day's minutiae, all of which were thoroughly irritating even though they had not yet occurred. Tossing and turning, throwing herself about, she finally crashed into the irritating realization of her insomnia, which for the rest of a horrible night was her catastrophic subject for contemplation and complaint.

So Jane's life revolved in a whirl of tremendous trifles like a phonograph needle caught in one groove.

There are so many women who develop essentially this same attitude, faced as they are by the hard job of housekeeping and homemaking.

● *How the Immaturity of Anger Is Conditioned*

Anger, like fear, is an instinct that is present at birth. In primitive man there was some survival value in the fear-anger mechanism. Those of our ancestors who were not pugnacious and angry when cornered did not survive. As civilization has progressed, the fear-anger mechanism is no longer essential, but man still has it. Today it constitutes a liability in a world where intelligent action is tremendously more valuable than angry action, and must be subdued and reconditioned.

Like fear, anger is further and almost unavoidably conditioned after birth into robust vigor. The new-born infant flies into a rage, instinctively at first, when its primitive wants, such as hunger, are not being met. A few tantrums that bring results condition the infant to use it further, precisely because it does bring results.

There is also a second important conditioning. Blowing its top in the face of the frustration of wanting something also conditions the infant to blowing its top in the face of frustration caused by any situation it is incapable of handling.

Such anger in an infant is considered to be normal. But as the child gets older, fits of rage, anger, and tantrums are considered less normal and much less desirable. We try to teach the growing child not to have tantrums.

A child illustrates the first type of purposeful conditioning when it screams, yells, and pounds its head on the floor until it is given its playmate's toy which it wanted very badly. It displays the second type of frustrated conditioning when it screams with rage because it cannot get a cover off a box, or open a door to a closet.

Whenever an adult gets angry one or the other of these two conditionings is usually involved. The purposeful type of conditioning is illustrated when a wife goes into a rage, until she gets her way, because her husband consistently neglects to put away his clothes. The second type of conditioning is involved when a husband becomes violently angry over a domestic situation that frustrates him and makes him feel inadequate because he does not know how to deal with it—as well he might when a son continues to do something he has been told repeatedly not to do, or his wife, who is firmly opposed to gambling, discovers that he has been betting on the horses.

The primitive instinct to become angry whenever harm threatens also exists in the adult, and is still apt to pop out whenever a person is threatened with harm. This primitive instinct has also been so conditioned that we become angry when we see someone else being harmed. For instance, we feel a retaliative anger when we see a man beating a child or a horse.

But as a rule, adult anger is generally aroused by the first two conditionings mentioned above. Anger is either a method of getting our way, or it is a reaction of frustration in the face of inadequacy or acute inferiority. In either case the benefits of anger are outweighed by the undesirability of its occurrence and even more by its ineffectiveness as a solution to any problem.

● Anger Is Always Childish and Ineffective

There is seldom an adequate excuse for an adult to blow his top. It is a childish way to solve a problem, and its frequent occurrence is simply an evidence of gross immaturity.

If you should ever, in spite of your best efforts, find yourself about to pop into a rage, at least remember how foolish the mind becomes under the influence of anger, and do not do the thing you are prompted to do. The mind is reduced to such imbecility at the time that any retaliations you make while angry, either in word or deed, will appear utterly childish when you have returned to your right senses, and will make you wish you could retract them.

Napoleon walked quickly away from one of his officers who had committed a serious error, saying, "If I were not angry I would have you put to death." Montaigne relates that Caius Rabirius was condemned to death by Caesar. But Caius, as was his right, appealed his case to the people. The people turned Caius free, being influenced in their decision by the fierce anger Caesar had exhibited in making his.

The best way to handle an angry person is to act as though the person were not angry. No other course vexes him quite as much, nor better enables you to keep *your* head. The best contempt for anger is to meet it with complete tranquility and cool silence.

Daniel Webster was stopped in a speech one time by a man who berated him hotly in a fit of anger. Webster remained silent while the man exhausted his anger, then without paying the slightest attention to what had happened, continued with his speech at the place where he had left off.

A person who is frequently angry loses the basic respect of those about him. No one thinks very highly either of the opinions constantly delivered by a person in a state of anger, or of the person himself. Although a child may develop a fear of a person who is easily provoked to wrath, the child will also develop disdain for his decrees and disrespect for him.

● Do Not Resort to Angry Discipline with Children

Discipline in a family is absolutely essential. Woe to the family (and its children) in which there is little, or very poor, discipline, either because of parental weakness, or because parents have the theory that children's impulses should never be repressed lest the child thereafter lead a frustrated life.

We live in a complicated and demanding world in which getting along with others is the most important thing we have to learn. Bother with repressed impulses! Repressed impulses is another term for immaturities. Instead of fearing that we may repress impulses in discipline, we should be afraid that we shall arrest the development of maturity by having no discipline. In our kind of world we need to learn that others have rights equal to ours, that decency and consideration belong to others as well as ourselves. Learning that simple principle will repay the individual a thousandfold. Not to learn it inevitably leads to meanness and misery.

Many people think disciplining is of no value unless it is done in high anger. But angry disciplining is poor and ineffective disciplining. It is almost always unreasonable in the sense of not being directed in the proper direction, because the angry mind is not capable of discretion or intelligent action. Angry discipline is more childish than the matter being disciplined; it is the angry parent who most deserves discipline. The child, after its first scare or two, has enough sense to lose all its respect for opinions that are thrown off in the heat of anger, just as it has a declining regard for the person who throws them off. Angry threats accompanied by a slap, are finally regarded by the child as momentarily uncomfortable but of no great importance in the long run. Discipline by spanking and hitting is an act of anger. Did you ever hit a child without being angry? Angry disciplining is merely an admission of inadequacy in a parent.

Discipline should be an exercise of the intelligence rather than the emotion of anger.

As much as possible, discipline should be based on approvals more than on disapprovals. Children are very sensitive and responsive to the approbation and disapproval of those about them. They desire more than anything else to be loved and to be approved. They develop very abnormal reactions and ways if they receive constant disapproval.

To voice or show approval, warmly and sincerely, when a child acts well, will do more than voicing disapproval when a child misbehaves. "Mother was very proud to see you play so nicely with Kathryn and give her your dolls to play with. You are being a wonderful and a fine person." Or, "Bill, it was swell of you to walk your sister through the dark to the bus. You're developing into a peach of a guy. I'm all for you, kid." Such appreciation will do much more to develop increasing excellence on their own initiative than any amount of disapproval. When disapproval becomes necessary it should be on a reasonable, serious, but not angry, basis.

Jacky strikes angrily at his sister and says, "I hate you." That is the moment for nipping that attitude in the bud and not later after it has become a customary thing.

You say, "Jacky, there is no good reason ever to get angry and hit anyone like that. Suppose I did that to you? How would you like it? In this family we don't hit people like that. You go outside and run up and down until you've worked your anger off, and don't come in until you think you can be nice."

Children should not be allowed to quarrel more than once among themselves. "Children," the mother says, "quarreling is something that is never done in this family; everyone of you go to your room and close your door. When you have decided how you can play without quarreling you may come out."

But how useless such discipline would be in a family where father and mother quarrel frequently.

It is surprising how little disciplining is necessary in happy children living in a happy family where there is no parental stress, but where there is an example of parental unselfishness and consideration, and where children are kept creatively happy by a mother who knows her business. Parents of unhappy families will not believe this, but in a really happy family active disciplinary measures are not necessary once a week, and punishment twice for the same offense is seldom necessary.

Do not lower a child's self-esteem by angrily telling him that he's "bad," or that he is below other children in what can be expected of him, or that he has fallen into disrepute, or that he is not worthy. It is far more effective to appeal to his pride. An inferiority complex is the result of disparagement and life is hard enough without that additional handicap. The best approach is that the family thinks well of him and expects good, and so do other people.

This is especially important in a child who is slow and less capable than others. It is so easy to crush them with their shortcomings.

Discipline carried out in anger produces resentments, hatreds, and fears in children that not only make more disciplining increasingly necessary, but materially hinders the development in the child of more mature attitudes.

If you are moved to hurt someone while you are angry, let it be yourself. Put your tongue between your teeth where it will remain silent, and bite it hard.

Instead of childishly allowing every wave of frustration to sweep you into a state where you deserve to bite yourself, develop the mature, intelligent attitude that you can rise above anger and gain a purpose or meet a frustration more maturely and effectively by using good common sense.

● Learn to Say "Nuts" to Irritations

One of the most inspiring moments in American history occurred through the appropriate use of the word "nuts."

And the appropriate use of the word "nuts" at the right times in your own life can be equally inspiring.

It was in those miserable moments when the German Army under General von Rundstedt had an American Army trapped and surrounded in the Battle of the Bulge. The Americans were stiff with cold and without possibility of help because a heavy fog had for days prevented any kind of relief from the air. General von Rundstedt demanded the unconditional surrender of the apparently overwhelmed American troops.

The answer General Anthony McAuliffe sent back to the German General was the single, marvelously apt word, "Nuts!"

"NUTS!" It's a wonderful word for back talk in any situation. You can drag it out with the grand air of Macbeth when you defiantly face the fouled bottom of a greasy pan—"Nuts to you, foul pan, thou canst not shake me from my purpose!" There is a lot of fun in a little imagination, and a lot of imagination in a little fun.

You should constantly handle irritations without getting upset, so that it becomes a mature habit you do not need to think about.

Until it does become your habitual attitude you first of all need to form the determination not to be irritated or angry by the things that happen.

Secondly, you must keep an eye on your reactions and not let them get out of hand. When you see something coming up that has an irritation or anger potential in it, say to yourself:

"Nuts! I do not need to let this get under my skin."

Then proceed to handle it with equanimity.

This maturity, like any of the others, is yours once you appreciate its value and institute a determined effort to practice it. As the practice proceeds, it gradually becomes a habitual and permanent attitude.

8

Having a Tenderness and Compassion for Things Human

Those fortunate enough to be sound in body, and reasonably sound in mind, have cause to sing a continual little song in some quiet nook of themselves, a grateful, simple little ditty that should trill along without interruption like the song of the wood thrush in the cathedral-like silence of deep woods.

There are *so* many unfortunates in this world. There are those who carried their misfortunes into the world at birth, a club foot, a shriveled arm, a hydrocephalus. Others received a life-long handicap in their childhood, in adolescence, or in adult life. They are the blind, the maimed, the sick, the crippled, the mentally ill. Who is to say which of these is most unfortunate?

The unfortunates have their own standards of relative values. The blind man is glad he has his arms. The amputee is glad he can see. I know a crippled, helpless man who told me, laughingly, that he was glad he could not contract the vices nor get about to do the evil deeds he might if he were hale and hearty.

● The Greatest Personal Misfortune Is to Be Cruel

But the most unfortunate person of all, more unfortunate than all others, is the person with a crippled personality; he who is crippled in having no feeling for things human. He has no tender appreciation that every human being has aspirations, dreams and needs, often deep scars that hurt, often sores that

134

pain, high desires that have been killed or are dying, or just plain, simple needs for friendship and help in getting food and making a living.

This crippled personality is the cruel, mean person, the hostile individual, the person insensitive to the feelings of others.

Such a person is cruel for the same reason a child can be so cruel. He can inflict harm and suffering without flinching or blinking an eye because he has not developed that sixth sense which detects the feelings other people have, that every person has.

● Cruelty Is the Worst of All Vices

Cruelty is the lowest of all the immaturities. If you wish to use the word "vice," cruelty is the worst of all vices. The worst kind of cruelty is that a person should do harm solely for the pleasure of seeing it done, without deriving any personal advantage from it.

In the course of human history we have come to expect a certain amount of cruelty in men. A cruel *man* has always been regarded as still being a man. But not so a cruel woman. A cruel woman, in the past, was usually considered to be a witch or a demon.

Cruelty has even been condoned in some places, and in some ages, as a quality of strength, ruthless but necessary in men, especially in great men who took charge of governments, the men who have managed to keep Western civilization in a continual, nonsensical state of war or preparation for war.

● Cruelty a Prominent Feature in Man's Past

Like the other immaturities, the immaturity of cruelty, or hostility, or just plain insensitivity, has persisted through history down to the present. It was probably much more prevalent and pronounced in earlier times than it is today. As recently as the 16th century, Michel de Montaigne felt it necessary to apologize in his writings for his feeling of compassion for all things, human as well as non-human, because it was so contrary to the traditional attitude expected of a man in his day. In Montaigne's time, and long after his death in 1592, it was still common to accuse women of witchcraft and men of being in league with the devil. To obtain their admission of guilt, ghastly tortures were used which included such refinements as breaking their legs and arms, then burning them alive at the stake in a great public spectacle, either singly or *en masse*, sometimes 40 or 50 at a time, the thousands of spectators singing hymns until the bodies were consumed by the fire. Then the spectators turned to the improvised food shops set up for the occasion, and to the souvenir stalls for mementos and holy reminders of the occasion.

Such practices of unbelievable cruelty were common throughout Europe. During medieval times untold thousands of people (people like you and me) were publicly burned alive at the stake, hung in public display, or boiled alive, with hardly ever an audible murmur from those who professed belief in the brotherhood of man.

In ancient times cruelty was even more pronounced; it was condoned by governments and the people, especially by their leaders and by the male heads of families. Many ancient religions used human sacrifices in their rites.

Cruelty has always been a prominent feature in man's treatment of man. As Adam Smith remarked, "Man is a wolf to man."

● **Cruelty Still Present in the Contemporary Scene**

In modern times public cruelty has, on the whole, become less harsh, more refined, and cloaked in less abhorrent forms. Our era points (with pride?) to the treatment of the Negro and the American Indian in the United States; to the Nazi horrors at Buchenwald and Lidice; to the mass purges and deportations to Siberia; to our own mass bombings at Nagasaki and Hiroshima.

We are not as mature and civilized as we like to think. We are not rid of cruel men in high places, nor of cruel ideas in society. But I like to think, and there is evidence to support the belief, that we are gradually getting better, gradually growing more mature, less cruel, and that a deep feeling for things human is becoming more prevalent.

● Cruelty Is Weakness, Not Strength

We have always mistakenly regarded cruelty as a certain kind of strength; we see this idea expressed in boys playing bad men; in men going into forests killing deer and rabbits, more for sport than food, and bragging about it as though it were "manly"; in businessmen forcing competitors out and against the wall.

Yet nothing could be further from the truth than that cruelty is strength. Actually, cruelty is the immaturity of a great weakness, an inability to handle a situation with real effectiveness. It is simply the failure of not having matured into an effective adult. The really strong man has no need to resort to cruelty or inhumanity; he can accomplish more, both for himself and for everyone else, by intelligent measures which do not include inhumanity.

● Cruelty Can Now Annihilate the Human Race

Cruelty is being gradually bred out of the human race by the very conditions now being imposed by our social environment. Perhaps at one period of man's early experience cruelty was necessary for the survival of the race, just as it might be said that cruelty is a necessary aid in the survival of fish, wild mammals, and insects.

The conditions that exist in human society today are such that the future of man, indeed the very survival of man, specifically requires that cruelty of every kind be relegated to the scrap heap of obsolescence, that human strength henceforth lies in understanding our mutual problems, and sensing the needs of human beings, whether they exist in China, Africa, or the United States. The shrinking of the earth's size due to amazingly rapid transportaion, the development of weapons capable of wiping *us all* out, make it mandatory that cruel, egotistical and selfish men be spotted and labeled as the immature children they are before they assume control of governments, whether in America or England, in Germany, Russia, or in the rest of the world.

We have arrived at the period in the human enterprise

where mutual aid and mutual understanding alone can save us, where cruelty and unfeeling indifference to things human can at last destroy us all.

The state of the world is at the critical juncture where there is no *CAUSE* more important and necessary for every person to espouse, whether he is a tiller of the fields or the head of a government, than the welfare and happiness of people, all the people, in every place. This point of view, this practical ethics, has virtually become a *must* in present-day human living if we are to survive.

● *The Maturity of Tenderness for Things Human*

The maturity that is the opposite of the immaturity of cruelty, hostility and insensitivity to others, is the maturity of tenderness and compassion for things human. This maturity consists of the attitude and feeling that every individual has not only the right to a good life, but a good chance to find it, and the conviction that by the proper use of human power and knowledge every individual can attain a good life.

The maturity of tenderness and compassion begins with human considerations at the family level and concerns the members of our family; it grows to include the people of our community, and comes into full flower when it encompasses every person in every land. Returning to our definition of a maturity as "an attitude that will benefit ourselves as well as those associated with us," this is the only attitude that will fulfill the terms of the definition in this particular field of human reference.

Although much in history is the story of inhuman and clumsy cruelty, history also contains the story of the slow but gradual evolution of compassion and tenderness, such as the gradual dissolution of the once-universal institution of slavery; the gradual replacement of cruel, inhuman, irresponsible governments with government by the consent of, and for the good of, the governed; the steady growth of the security, the rights, and the dignity of the common man. While it is true that much that is cruel still remains in the world, it is also true that the general underlying feeling of people the world over is in the direction of greater consideration for the individual. If the human race can escape the present critical danger of self-annihilation, I feel certain it will mature in this, and that the universal concern for people as people will grow stronger, that this concern will be the primary motive of governments and of society as a whole, and the individual will be the important center.

● The Emancipation of Woman and Woman's Mind

A striking part of this gradual evolution of tenderness for things human has been the emancipation of women in the past 150 years. This has happened largely because women at last came to be recognized as human beings; at the same time woman's mind became an influential force. For the first time in history, woman's mind is coming into its own, is expressing itself freely, and is making itself felt.

Woman's mind, conditioned by the biological role of motherhood, has always veered toward tenderness and compassion. These are the very ingredients which the world so needs today. Having them, woman becomes a new and vital force in the human enterprise, one sorely needed.

The male mind has tended to be aggressive and acquisitive in the direction of economic and political power, ends which have been raised to such an importance that they have justified any means, even cruelty. In its over-all tendency the male mind has accentuated material and physical values, the female mind human and individual values.

We need, of course, the combination of the male and female mind and outlook, just as much and in as real a way as we need the physical union of the male and female body. We have been too long arriving at this conclusion, failing to realize that their differences in outlook complement each other in a way we have a great need of.

We need the one as much as the other. We need the male's good points — the courage to meet and overcome obstacles, the ambition to accomplish great things, the ability to reason analytically and synthetically. But these good points do not require — in fact they can only flourish without — ruthlessness and cruelty. He does not need to stomp all over human values in the practice of his good points.

But now more than ever we need the woman's good points too. The time has arrived in human evolution when human values must become the primary consideration in determining and guiding whatever man, any man, does. The square-jawed, keen-edged, hairy-chested prototype of Kit Carson can still be our ideal, but he needs to be equipped, not with a gun, but with a motivation that is primarily for the good of the race, and with an intelligence that is aware and cognizant of human values. The traditional picture of the strong man — held up to us long before the advent of the virtuous knight of old — has always shown him as too ruthless, cruel, and unfeeling. As an ideal it should be dropped like a hot brick. The picture of the strong man should become instead the capable, accomplished, intelligent man who is also provided with compassion and tenderness. No longer the noise of clashing swords and booming of guns, but the music of poetry and the dance should be heard, the general acclaim of great and good accomplishments, the music that accompanies good living.

● **The Maturity of Tenderness Comes Easily to Women**

Here, then, is a maturity that is tailor-made for women, one that it is much easier for them to acquire than it is for men. Through the ages a common cliché about women has always been that they are chicken-hearted. It is the rare woman who has not developed at least a fair degree of tenderness and compassion for human things.

It is necessary for a woman to realize that men do not come by this maturity easily. First of all, they do not have, as women do, the conditioning of the biological role of bearing and rearing children. Secondly, in our culture, as in most all cultures, the ideal presented to boys — in our games, in stories, in comic books, on television, radio, and the movies — is that they should be hard and strong; they are the hunters and it is the part of a man to kill the animals of field and stream not so much for food but for the glory of what is called being a sportsman. They are providers, and to provide well they must beat tough competition at every stage. To accomplish this they must not be pansies, must not cringe from stepping on someone's toes, must not hesitate to take a job or a bankroll from someone else—providing they stay within the law, of course, or at least no further from it than a successful lawsuit. The sensitive, dreaming, poetical boy is usually the one who has discovered human values. He has a hard time adjusting the traditional ideal of the masculine to a great feeling for things human.

After her marriage a woman often finds that her mate is inconsiderate, often blind to her needs, or not understanding of the children. He is not what one could call physically cruel, but he comes mighty close to being mentally cruel. In fact he actually does manage this occasionally.

In this, as well as in the related overlapping maturities of egoism, selfishness (No. 3) and moody disposition (No. 1), men are apt to be children. But fortunately for wives, most of our men in this age and in this country are unfeeling rather than downright cruel. Twice the pity for the wife who has married a man who is actually cruel.

If the man is otherwise fairly mature, or has a quick, facile mind, she may, through adroit suggestion and undercover pedagogy, teach him some of the elements of understanding human beings and human needs. This, of course, must be done cautiously and without ever intimating that he isn't as wonderful as he thinks he is, without puncturing his ego, without ever letting him know his wife actually is trying to improve him.

But don't expect too much. In fact, expect nothing, and verily you will not be disappointed. Don't forget that he is, and will probably always be, a very egotistical male. It would be necessary for him to learn a great deal of understanding, sympathy, and tenderness for other humans before he could lose his egoism.

But go ahead, work on him. It will be a happy experience.

Don't give up right away. And do be careful! He has an ego!

9

Finding Work and Responsibility
a Joy and Pleasure

Maturity No. 7

One of the most amusing errors of our time, one that goes
way back in history, is the misconception that it is the man
who does the hard work and the woman who merely keeps
house.

It is a discovery of this century, made perhaps by some
obscure professor of sociology who may have tried housework
as an experiment, that, viewed from almost any angle you
please, a woman's work (at least where there are children) is
harder than the work the average man has to do.

The reduction of the wife's work by labor-saving devices
and by better designing of houses has been very real. But it has
been offset, and possibly more than offset, by higher standards
of living, the maintenance of which requires more work, and
by the almost complete dearth of servant help for the modern
housewife.

What in the world has happened to the old-fashioned hired
girl?

They were annihilated by universal high school education.
What little domestic help one can manage to drag in is hard
to find and costs $1.50 to $2.00 an hour, and you need that
kind of money to balance an already shaky budget.

The thing that strikes the foreigner who visits our homes is how elegantly we live, how fine our homes are, how well prepared and sumptuous our meals, how clean everything is kept, how excellently everything about the house is run, how smartly pert the lady of the house appears; *and yet SHE does all the work, single-handed, without servants.* A young man from India visiting in such an American home said, "In India my mother has two servants. If she had to run a place like this, she would have three."

That remark made the mother of the house very proud. It helped her to do the dishes. (Appreciative remarks from the husband help quite as much.)

We middle-class Americans (and that includes a big part of America) have developed such a high standard of living, fine houses, fine comforts, fine meals that we are running our poor housewives ragged trying to keep up the show.

The only possible thing one could do is what no one seems to want to do. That is to lower our standard of living and go back to plain floors, plain hardwood furniture, and nothing much around. Cutting down on the standard of living would be a partial answer which no family seems to want merely to save mother some work. It would mean a less well-kept house, not as neat, curtains not kept as beautifully nor washed as often, woodwork unwaxed, floors scrubbed and rugs vacuumed less, bedrooms untidy, simpler meals less carefully prepared.

It could be done and save a lot of work. But no one in the family would want it after having had what we've had.

● No One but a Housewife Knows How Much Work a Home Is

No one can understand how much, much work a house and family are until he tries it.

A young married woman with one child, a college graduate, and an erstwhile secretary to a geologist, who had assumed before marriage that housework was a trifling nothing, asked,

"What is wrong with me? I am up at 6:30 every morning, keep going as fast as I can without sitting down once except to feed myself and the baby, and at 11 at night I'm still ironing!

And I've got everything organized to death. What am I going to do when I have more than one child?"

The experienced housewife she had asked threw back the answer, "My dear, your grandmother and her grandmother had exactly the same trouble. Think nothing of it. The angel taking care of scullery maids will see that you stay on your feet even when you have four children. Somehow, some way, by some hook or crook, we poor wives manage to live through it all. You will, too, without needing to work much beyond 11 at night or starting much before 6:30 in the morning. You will get it all into a nice, long, steady day. Two pieces of advice: don't drop; and, like it!"

It's easy for a woman faced with her everlasting task—tired yet not daring to stop—to become downright disgusted with the whole proposition, to be aggravated by its minutiae. She can get as irritated and agitated over it as a cross little boy who goes along giving every pebble in his path a good swift kick into oblivion.

● The Irksome Side to Housekeeping

The *amount* of housework is irksome enough. But it really becomes irksome if you add to that the *time* involved—the steady grind, day after day, Sundays and holidays. Now, to this irksome mess add this sauce—the distressing fact that pops into your mind everytime you think of what you'd *rather* be doing but haven't had time to do; the distressing fact that *everything* you do could be done by the lowest kind of domestic servant, by a simple "hired girl," by a scullery maid. That irks too. It irritates. Here you are, with a fine education, and in all your huffing and puffing you're accomplishing what any servant could do. To this matrimony has dedicated you, has dragged you— to washing dirty pots and pans and dishes, to picking up baby's things, children's things, husband's things, things that don't seem to belong to anybody but seem always to be out of place.

Another thing that irks when you start thinking the wrong way about what you might have been, might have done, is how nice men have it with an eight-hour day and Saturday and Sunday off, while your day literally never ends, continues on into the wee hours when baby needs a bottle, and a long rocking for the colic. He too, lucky he, has a job that is interesting, *and* important, that counts for something more than getting pots and pans scoured and running around endlessly in the same old rat race.

● One of a Wife's Greatest Assets—The Ability to Work

Housekeeping continues to be so much hard work that a wise young man will do well to rate ability to work in a prospective wife higher than beauty or wealth.

This wisdom was precociously developed in a lad of eleven whom I once had as a patient because he had severely frozen both hands while on his way to country school on a bitterly cold morning. On telling him that he would be unable to go to school for a month, he seemed very displeased. I said:

"I never saw a boy before who liked to go to school. You must have a girl at school."

He admitted he had.

"What is her name?"

He sheepishly refused to tell.

"Is she pretty?," I asked.

"No, she isn't pretty," was his surprising answer.

"Is she rich?," I persisted.

"No, she isn't rich."

"Are you expecting to marry this girl?"

"Yes, I am," he said very positively.

"Well, if she isn't pretty, and isn't rich, why are you going to marry her?"

"She's a good worker," was his factual, straightforward reply.

Perhaps the fact that women work harder than men is a rediscovery, rather than a discovery. Long ago it had been discovered by a man living in Munduqumor Society on the Yuat River. It occurred to him one day that the women did *all* the work in Munduqumor, including all the food-getting, leaving men free to plot, fight, enjoy the shade, practice dancing, and demonstrate their manhood by bringing home heads. This man, as soon as he had announced his discovery, was publicly executed as a feminist and dangerous character. His discovery died in the making.

● Will Housework Ever Be Made Easy?

The discovery that housekeeping is one of the hardest of all careers is moving extremely slowly in bringing about any change for the better. There are as yet comparatively few men who believe it. There are those, of course, who never believe anything, especially this. If the day arrives when enough men believe it, something will be done about it, but even then it will not come as quickly as it would if men had to do housework themselves.

It will take *men* to reduce the amount, the strenuous character, and the hours of housework; not that we mean to imply that it is they and not the women who have the brains to do it. The important thing is that it is men who have the incentive. Work, or rather doing away with work, has always been a challenge to men. So much so that, as in this case, they are interested even though the work belongs to someone else. Women left to themselves will endeavor to do nothing about a problem like this. That is because they really expect nothing else, and think no other course possible than work. Even long before Munduqumor Society flourished on the banks of the Yuat, women and work were inseparable and indistinguishable from each other. It is only today, in this age of all sorts of revolutionary awakenings, that she begins to feel the faint stirrings of a doubt. But even today, as in times past, women accept work as their natural lot, and when they see it before them, they roll up their sleeves and keep them up until it is done.

But not so with men. Men react differently to work. Through history men faced with work have first made fine speeches eulogizing both work and workmen, and have then fussed around figuring out some easy way of getting it done, or possibly some way of getting around it, or if they are at home, some excuse for getting out of the house without doing it. This incentive to invent a way to escape exertion has stimulated more progress than has even men's everlasting incentive for blowing each other up. There has been many a man, for instance, who has worked strenuously for long hours, trying to figure out a way of picking a thread off a rug without bending over. As a result, women are now blessed with the vacuum cleaner; this they tease out of an overfilled closet, spend 15 minutes to find the hose and the necessary attachments, put it all together four different ways before it fits, lug it in to the rug, reverse the whole procedure, including getting everything back into the closet, and very easily get the thread picked up.

When sociologists, city planners, engineers, efficiency experts, and politicians really get down to the business of reducing housework, you may be sure they will definitely come up with something—what we cannot accurately predict—but it will have to be something revolutionary to bring any relief. It may possibly take the direction of doing away with housework altogether, which is not as impossible as it sounds. This could be done by regarding our present system of family units as ridiculously inefficient and wasteful of both energy and material, and putting the whole matter of the *family in society* on a sort of assembly line basis in huge, well-aired, well-lit, tapestried assembly plants where all that needs to be done is accomplished for everyone with push-buttons and machinery. So as not to lose the benefits of the family plan, the tool room cubicle idea as it now exists in manufacturing plants could be extended and enlarged; lovely storage compartments could be used from which—should you be so inclined in your leisure— you could draw your children by handing a man your number.

Seriously though, housework is in for some kind of change. Perhaps you and I will never see it in our day. But when it comes (and it is gradually on the way even now) housework will be revolutionized. Look what we have done to the horse and buggy, to the candle, and to the "hired girl"; all were once regarded as immutable institutions but now are gone. But, until housework meets the same fate, we'll have to face it, and continue to face it. So let's do just that.

● The Woman Who Marries Must Face It

As the family plan and housework are set up at the present time, the girl who works for a living before marriage can look forward to doing two or three times as much work taking care of a home, husband, and children. And two or three times is a very conservative estimate.

The clause "for better or for worse" was not an idea of the moment slipped into the ceremony to sound mysterious. It is very definitely a fair warning that the bliss may not be unmitigated, that things may not turn out altogether as they seem. It is a ministerial intimation to the girl—gay, happy and lighthearted—that tomorrow she meets her nemesis, tomorrow she launches on a course of work, pure work, simple work, work that with each new child is apt to grow worse and possibly never better. One thing we are sure of and one thing she can be sure of: she is in for it, irrevocably and surely, as the minister hurries over the warning "for better or for worse" and pronounces them man and wife.

The man can still get out of it. He can manage, if he is adroit, to find no work, neither the kind he is fitted for nor the kind he thinks would fit him. The search for work, properly managed, can be stretched through years of leisure.

But let the woman try to get out of work and see what happens! A family can get along for quite a while without the man working by living on relief, off relatives, on the cuff, or on the wife's outside work. But let the woman get the idea of stopping her housework; the chances are it means the finish, the annulment, the end. Even during the Depression of the early 30's, when men generally took an extended holiday (perhaps depressions are fiendishly invented by men for that purpose) woman's work went on as before or possibly even more intensively than before, for now her problems were increased by such matters as trying to stretch a pound of hamburger through three meals or drawing out half an apple into a pie.

Moralists, who find bad reasons why other people should do good things, have written so much and given so many reasons why men should work, that it confirms our suspicion that a great many people down through the ages have basically and flatly disliked work; from the great amount of writing that extolls the home and the sterling value of a mother's work, we may suspect that some of these people may have been women. As a matter of record, I have had women tell me quite frankly that they did *not* like housework.

● Liking to Work Is a Maturity

That, of course, is a tragedy. It is bad enough to have to work, but it is ten times worse to have to work hard and long and always *without in the least liking it*. That constitutes living in a trap, a trap so dreadful that there are not enough invectives in the language to describe it. The things that come to mind right off as worse than such a life is being pregnant 15 times with little interval, or having a husband with a nasty, grouchy disposition.

Having to work without liking it "drieth up the bones" as the psalmist put it mildly. It drieth up considerably more than bones. It drieth up the humor, and the heart, one's mind, one's enthusiasm, pleasures, dreams; in short, one's living.

Since you can't get out of housework, and since men have not yet gotten around to annihilating it, the trick, obviously, *is to learn to like work!*

The most mature attitude to enable the housewife to meet her problem is the attitude of simply liking work and responsibility.

It was expressed by the experienced housewife telling the young mother who was working from 6 A.M. to 11 P.M., "Two pieces of advice: don't drop, and like it."

It was expressed somewhat differently by a wonderful woman who had brought up nine fine children and had helped her husband in the barn and in the fields.

She was asked, "Don't you ever get tired?"

Her answer was, "I learned 25 years ago never to ask myself that question.   I always told myself instead that I liked work, that in fact I was crazy about it."

As we have reiterated often, a maturity is something you cannot attain without *learning* it. We do not start out mature. We have to *learn* ways of turning an adult situation or problem like housework into a benefit for ourselves, rather than into a trouble and tribulation. Of all the maturities there is none any more important to a woman, and also to a man, than the maturity of liking work.

Most children, being immature, do not like to work, and if they should be prodded into work—by hook, by crook, by wheedling or force—they most thoroughly and obviously dislike it. There is however a peculiar thing you may have noticed about children: they hate, worse than castor oil, to do a certain job around home, but they highly enjoy doing the same job at the neighbor's. Why is that? Over at the neighbor's, doing that particular job makes them feel important and grown-up. If you can make them feel as important and grown-up at home, you have an excellent chance of getting them to do the same work, as pleasantly as they did at the neighbor's. Some mothers have a knack for this kind of thing. It's easier with some children than others, and it's usually easier with girls than with boys.

● A Housewife's Work Is Important

The behavior of children gives us the first clue as to how to teach ourselves to like work, particularly housework. We must begin to look at our work as something that gives us some importance; a different and more dignified importance than what you feel when you are faced with three baskets full of wet wash that will not dry, a closet full of moths, a sink full of yesterday's dishes, a boy in bed sick with measles, and a baby soiled from head to foot.

You need to find for yourself and for your work an importance that is at once *big* and *true,* an importance beyond the necessity of drying the wash, doing the dishes, de-mothing the closet, nursing the boy, and cleaning the baby.

After all, you and your work *are* important!

You know it is true. You tend to forget it when you become swamped with minutiae that seem utterly absurd. Once in a while it is a good thing to breathe a little assurance to yourself, "Of course I'm important, and this is an important job, in spite of the wash, in spite of the dishes, and other things."

It is a feeling that you should have all the time—as you stir the cake, as you fill the laundry tub, so that at all times it is a part of you—that you have the most important job in the world.

And you have.

Let us assume you are doing a creditable job creating a good home, that you are successful in making it a place of human comfort, that you are making the physical plant a thing of beauty and a joy forever. Let us also assume that you are succeeding, with your husband, in making your marriage a mutually agreeable companionship of well-grounded affection, and a solidly enduring friendship of understanding. And to complete your fortune, let us assume you have two, three, or even four average (let us be reasonable) enthusiastic youngsters; the last we refuse to qualify with superlatives beyond saying they are all right in the ways a human being should be all right. Let us suppose, in short, your home is the kind of place you *can* make it.

This *you* have made. This is *your* creation, infinitely more than it is your husband's. Without you and without your work—without the dishes, without the cooking, the laundry, the bedmaking and the other scullery—it simply couldn't exist. This place exists, let us not forget, because of you.

What would life be like without the housewife? Now let us imagine your life, your husband's and your children's lives, without it. Blot out completely this home you have made. Imagine for a few moments (picture to yourself, if you will, sitting there in your chair) what a void, what an abyss of unrequited need there would be in your lives if it simply ceased to exist. Would any of you prefer some other center of existence? Imagine your husband as he left his work, imagine yourself as you left a store, imagine your children after school, going to a rooming house or a hotel. Something extremely valuable and something extremely important would have dropped out of all your lives. As a matter of fact, as you think about it, the *most* valuable and the *most* important attachment and substance any of you have in your individual lives would have disappeared. We are not going to wax sentimental over the home (there has been enough of that), but it is impossible to overestimate what the home you make means in the lives of you and your husband, and especially in the lives of your children.

The house is the center of living. It is your labor, your constant round of cleaning, adjusting, and fixing, that makes those rooms of yours that looked *so* bare before you moved in, a cheerful, pleasant, and smoothly-managed center (make no bones about it—*CENTER*), *the* very vital center, of all your lives. This is the center of your thinking and your living; your base of operations, your refuge in a storm, your shelter in a rain; a place to lounge, to eat, to sleep, a place to store and use your precious possessions; it is practically the whole of your living. It is the place where you are free to move about, free to create your enjoyments, free to entertain, to find recreation, to read, to watch TV, to bathe, to smoke, to be congenial, to cooperate, to smile and be smiled at, to have problems and to solve them, and all the nuances and all the complexities that go into the meaning of a CENTER of living.

Take this center out of our lives and where could any of us find any kind of a substitute to replace it? Your husband's club? You and he know how poor that would be! A room there wouldn't begin to compare with all that he has at home; just the matter of his belongings and his individual possessions, the power tool, the books, the guns and fishing rods that are distributed in their proper places all over the house; think of all the other services, all the other niceties, the comforts, all the companionship, affection, consideration, esteem he has at home and would not have in a room at the club.

"Home," as Robert Frost put it in his poem, *The Death of the Hired Man,* "is the place where, when you have to go there, they have to take you in."

But it is far more than that. It is the place that affords you a base of operations, to which you return to replenish your strength and spirit. It is the place where you can get a lift when you need a lift, and where you can recharge your battery, refuel, refurbish, revitalize.

But it is much more than that. It is the place where all of you can find the many items sufficient living includes: such inner needs as a sense of security, affection, creative expression, recognition, companionship, usefulness, belonging, new experiences, self-esteem, and the needs of the outer man for food, clothing, shelter, bathing, polishing shoes, combing hair, rest (yes, I said rest).

It is, when you come to think of it, a most marvelous and tremendous institution, the exact likes of which does not exist on earth, except as the similar institutions of other families. Without question, it is the most valuable invention human ingenuity has yet devised, and you are the person who is its creator, its high Mogul, its manager. How much more fortunate, how much more of an important figure, do you want to be?

These things we have mentioned barely begin to catalogue the more obvious meanings that your labor holds for your family.

You are in charge of the center of living. You and your husband (leaving the children out for the moment) bring into each other's lives biological and psychological fulfillments whose intrinsic value to you both is limited only by your capacities to make them rich. These values you and your husband create between you (remember now, we're assuming you are doing a good job as the prime mover); these relations you create in the home are as varied, as easy to manipulate, as pleasant, as comfortable, are more complete and more meaningful than any other relation you could possibly have, or have had, with any other human being, not excepting your mother. You and your husband form mankind's most successful cooperative enterprise. This statement remains true even after you allow for all the marriages that are unsuccessful. What other human enterprise has been more successful or more cooperative, any less punctured by exceptions? And what would your marital relation amount to without your own place to live; what if you didn't work and iron shirts, didn't cook meals, make beds, keep the house clean and inviting? It is your scullery as well as your intelligent capacities that makes possible the life you enjoy together. It would all be a flop without your efforts in providing the center where the two of you can live.

● You Make Your Husband the Kind of Man He Is

The kind of husband you have depends as much on your abilities as on the kind of man he is. The kind of human being he becomes, the worth he has as a man, is likewise in considerable part your making. The woman goes a long way in making the man, and a capable woman can make a capable man. Many a prominent figure has been put and held where he is by a buttressing wife. Don't forget, too, that he contributes mightily to your development if he is a capable man. You are a team, but *you* are the driver of the team, an unostentatious and invisible driver if you are a good one. You help him in hundreds of ways, psychologically and physically, in ways no one else could help him. Just in the matter of the entertaining his business or professional career requires—you entertain his friends, his associates, his hoped-for influences. You had both better stop to think, at least once a year when you are tired of your work, and he thinks he is tired of his lot, how utterly empty living would be for both of you if suddenly you did not have each other, and suddenly didn't have this center for living you call home.

Important as you are to your husband and as he is to you, and your home to both of you, they cannot compare with the importance this center of living you have created is to your children. You, and your work, are absolutely essential in raising your family of children.

What an important responsibility you have there! Your husband's job fades into insignificance beside it; he is in town merely making automobiles whereas you are home creating human beings. The two cannot compare, really. Creating *worthy* human beings, seeing them properly cared for physically, mentally, emotionally, tending to all their needs, teaching fundamentals, instilling proper habits and attitudes they are going to need as adults—all this is the most responsible and demanding work any human being has or can have.

● *Lady, Yours Is the Important Work*

Important? Lady, frankly and surely, without undue emphasis, there is no one more important than you, there is no place more important than your home, and there is no work more important than your work. There are some people who may be handling gigantic sums of money, or managing huge engineering projects, directing thousands of people, or charting the course of a nation, but none of them are doing a more important and significant work than you are, even though *they* occupy the limelight. Your job requires just as much skill, insight, and intelligence as their jobs do, and more than most; yours probably requires more time and more energy. There is no job worth the salt that doesn't require overtime and more endurance at times than one believes oneself to have. As an old proverb has it, *"He who never does more than he gets paid for, never gets paid for any more than he does."*

In these few ways, and in many more ways that you can think of yourself, the homemaker can be proud of her accomplishments and achievements, proud of being a glorified, world-moving, scullery maid.

● *Take Pride in Running a Good Ship*

Leaving now the over-all importance of your job, and turning to lesser things, we cannot overlook the compensation which you receive through the satisfaction and pride of running a good ship, the immense satisfaction in seeing your house neat, clean, and beautiful. You and your husband both get an inward thrill and reward when someone says, "You have such a lovely home!"

It gives you an even greater lift, a sort of gleeful walking-on-the-clouds feeling, when your husband compliments you on a meal, or on how nice you look. These are commendations he is more apt to think of than how beautifully you keep house. But his easy satisfaction in living and staying at home are indications he appreciates that, even if he doesn't think to tell you. Your accomplishments and their accompanying joys stand out in the course of his day like pearls strung on a necklace. There is pleasure in seeing the brass-door knocker shine after you have polished it, a floor bright and clean after you have waxed it, a white, white wash hanging on the line, piles of neatly ironed linen, a well-dressed cherub of a baby (the list could go on and on indefinitely); practically all your labors result in visible, tangible improvement. There is probably no greater satisfaction than watching a hungry family dive into an excellent meal, except possibly the preparation of it.

● The Happiness of Being Useful

Nor must we overlook another asset that comes to anyone who, like the housewife, does useful work—the smooth, good feeling of just plain being *useful*, which is about as good a feeling as any in human experience. You would appreciate it more, of course, and not take it so easily for granted, if you have ever (as you haven't) had the unpleasant experience of living days, weeks, without being the slightest bit of use to anybody. Many of the psychologists who make up lists of the psychological needs that people require in their lives seem to overlook the necessity of feeling useful. They universally include the necessity of feeling that one "belongs." The feeling that one is useful is another step in the same direction.

If one were asked to name the most useful class of people in the world, there would be little question about naming the housewife to that honor.

We have listed a few of the things, inadequately and very partially catalogued, that shed a light of importance and value to housekeeping, a work that is endless, discouraging drudgery only if you allow your spirit to regard it as such.

You are more than half ruined, and your entire day a failure, if you allow yourself to go about your work with a defeatist, grumbling, dissatisfied spirit. Why spoil your day, why spoil your living, why make everyone else around you equally miserable, by adopting an attitude you do not need to have? There is only one good way to meet your work—any kind of work from housework to cleaning chimneys to running a corporation—and that is pleasantly, cheerfully and agreeably. If you as a wife and mother are incapable of bringing these voluntary elements to your work, you are failing in the over-all mission and fundamental purpose of your job, which is usefulness to the human beings in your family.

● *The Will to Find Pleasure in Work*

What is more, you are letting yourself down, dreadfully. Putting pleasure, cheer and agreeableness into one's work, is entirely a matter of the *will* to put it there and keep it there. It is one of those things that comes into being because *you* have brought it into being.

It is a great gift, easily acquired, and fruitful. Being pleased, cheerful, and agreeable during your work not only makes the work ten times easier, but reduces fatigue to a fourth, and gives the work a value high above its actual output. It is really remarkable that so valuable a commodity is so readily acquired and so universally available.

It is remarkable, and unbelievable to anyone who hasn't made the experiment, to see how much work can be done without tiring if one likes to work.

As a matter of fact, without even starting to work, disliking work will cause one to be tired. There is a sound physiological basis for this tiredness; it is provoked by the somatotrophic hormone of the pituitary gland which the constant emotion of dislike stimulates.

This trick of liking work is so very easy to acquire. It is like slipping into a coat that is lying beside you on a chair. It is there; you have simply to put it on. So effective, so easy. One marvels at the torture, the taciturn, grumbling, dissatisfied worker makes for himself and his unfortunate companions.

● *The Pleasure of Being Able to Work*

Another light that will shed a kindly glow on your work any-time you turn it on (and you should leave it on) is the thought that "I *can* work," that you are at least physically able to work, that you have arms that move without too much bursitis, a back that will at least bend despite a second degree lumbago, fingers not too knotted by osteoarthritis, eyes that see, ears that hear, and all the other hundred and one properly adjusted accoutrements required in everyday getting-around in a functional fashion. We need to keep in mind how basically lucky we are that we belong in the class of the able-to-work, and are not among the physically disabled, the handicapped, the sick. Physical health is one of the very finest possessions one can possibly have. It is well never to forget it, but to keep it pinned high on your list of "WHOOPEES."

● *And Finally, the Joy of Work for Work's Sake*

While you are feeling thankful and cheerful that you *can* work, try the final, all-out, frontal attack, which will give you a decisive victory over work once and for all time. This attack consists in the fundamental feeling of *liking work,* or as Carlyle phrased it, "Work for work's sake," the lovely connotations of the word "sake" making something of a mission or a crusade out of it. The feeling of pleasure in merely *working* has in it the feeling of the dignity of work, the feeling that you are not simply a worthless bum, the feeling of animal pleasure at moving, turning, feeling your breath slide in and out easily but a little faster as you hurry, feeling muscles tightening and working under the skin, the perspiration wetting your brow; it is a sort of joy like a doe bounding through the woods.

In "just plain liking to work" there is the feeling too that comes from realizing how much better off you are having something to do to keep you active, quite different from the feeling of being useful; there is the joy of productive *activity.* If you have ever engaged in prolonged inactivity, or in unproductive leisure, you know what we mean. You could not stand leisure for an appreciable length of time without being completely bored. Leisure can become much more irksome than any kind of work.

Finally, it is a wonderful thing merely to have something to do. You have something to do, but in addition it does some good, so very much good, in such a very durable way.

Tell yourself and keep telling yourself:

"How lucky and how pleased I am to be doing my work, even housework."

10

Getting into Your Life the Proper
Mixture of Fact and Fancy

Fact and fancy, or common sense and conjecture, are all mixed up and tangled together in a helter-skelter fashion in our world. Well over half the things the total population of the world believes are not true.

This is too bad. For the things a person believes that are not true lead in one way or another to trouble for the individual himself and eventually to trouble between people.

The human race will probably never be able to sift out the chaff of fancy and retain only the grain of truth. We do not presume to do so in this chapter.

We are interested here in the mature attitude toward fact and fancy a woman needs in her immediate world.

● Fancy Has Its Place Just as Common Sense Does

Fancy is not all bad, by any means, as long as it is recognized as being fancy.

Imagination (one of the forms of fancy) is the spring that has driven the mechanism of the human race. Even science, which is a pure form of common sense, would be stopped in its tracks if imagination did not construct the hypotheses which provide it with the stepping stones to knowledge.

160

The mature mind is capable of enjoying the fruits of fancy: the creative imagination of the poet and novelist, the visions of the artist, the conjectures of the theologian and the philosopher, the delightful sweeps of the composer.

But in the workaday world the mature mind resorts to fact and utilizes common sense as much as is humanly possible. There fancy is merely a spice, a flavor, a perfume, to make fact palatable. The more maturely a person can adhere to fact and common sense, the more successfully he will deal with the adult problems of the everyday world.

● Fancy Exists in a Number of Different Forms

There are several varieties of fancy, some good, some bad.

Two varieties, *imagination* and *creative imagination,* are excellent expressions of fancy. They are responsible for some of the finest things the race has. And, as stated above, neither common sense nor science could go very far if imagination did not provide hypotheses and theories as a basis for their action.

Another variety of fancy is known as *idealism,* the fruits of which are *ideologies.* Idealism can be good if it is moderated by common sense, or it can be about the worst thing for a person, or for the human race, if it isn't. We shall say something in this chapter about adopting ideals in the field of a woman's endeavors.

Another variety of fancy is *conjecture.* One form of this that is bad, very bad, is *gossip.* A woman must take a common sense stand on gossip, and we shall have something to say in this chapter on that. Two other forms of conjecture, philosophical forms, are *intuitive insight* and *mysticism.* This book is not concerned with them. You may indulge in them if you wish, but be careful. There is much criticism today that these lead to fallacy rather than to truth.

Then there is another variety of fancy that is just plain undesirable; this is known variously as *reverie, daydreaming,* or *"building castles in the air."*

● **Beware of Imagination Uncontrolled by Common Sense**

Imagination is one of the desirable varieties of fancy when it is used creatively. But it can be used poorly, too. Watch it!

The most common, flagrant misuse of imagination is this: Many people, men as well as women, desert common sense and resort to poor imagination over the matter of their health. They constantly imagine that they are in poor health, that they are developing a cancer, coming down with a cold, suffering from heart trouble, or fear they have 50 complications of 20 horrible diseases.

They awaken in the morning and ask themselves, "Where am I sick today?"

They belong to the *Symptom-A-Day-Club*, and they manage to feel rotten all day, every day.

One of the odd things about this clay of ours is that whenever one searches around for a pain, an itch, or some place that doesn't feel exactly right, one can always find it. This is entirely *normal*. But an imagination uncontrolled by common sense can magnify it and make something horrible of it.

Some people imagine they are in a constant state of poor health. Nothing inside them ever works right, and nothing will ever work right. They no more expect to feel well than you and I expect to grow younger.

It is really remarkable to what an extent feeling well from day-to-day depends simply on telling ourselves we feel fine.

● **Stay Away from Reverie or Daydreaming**

It is an excellent rule to keep away from the variety of fancy known as *reverie, daydreaming,* or *"building castles in the air."*

Reverie is an escape (and haven't we all thought of escape?) into an imaginary world equipped with everything you do not have in your real world, including lots of delightful leisure, Bermuda beaches with warm sun and cool breezes, the supposedly lush life of a cinema idol, and general overstuffed luxury.

Reverie creates a detachment from dishes, waxed floors, overdue payments on baby's clothes, the TV set, and the car;

it affords a relief from the sorry condition of your hair, and the miserable mess all over the house.

Reverie sounds wonderful, whether it is provided by simple daydreaming or by a candy diet enriched with romantic novels, TV programs, and the movies. On the surface at least, reverie looks like the answer to the unmitigated idiocy and colossal chore of housework. And it would be, except for the four short words, "It does not work."

Some women try to escape into reverie or daydreaming, but finally they run their heads into facts that are as damnably solid as a thick concrete wall. Dirty dishes have a cursed way of siding with fact and drawing cockroaches; snarling bill collectors have a way of pushing fact into your face and driving off with the TV set or the auto; fortunately, you have a legal hold on your baby, but the doctor and the hospital trying to collect their bills make you wonder whether you gave birth to the baby or whether they did. The mess your hair is in finally gets so bad the husband is either too frightened or too disgusted to live at home; and the disorder in the house that is left to itself deteriorates to the point of sheer and utter chaos.

Acting purely on the basis of fancy of any variety is bad, because sooner or later someone is going to be anything but benefited by it. Acting on the basis of ascertainable fact is usually safe; if it hurts anyone, it is because all the facts were not known or taken into consideration. But in the matter of fancy, more fancy does not become more beneficial, nor more protective from self-inflicted harm.

● **Beware of Conjecture in the Form of Gossip**

Gossip is a common way in which women sometimes resort to fancy and do incredible harm to people who are innocent, or additional harm to guilty people who, instead of another kick, need society's help.

It is doubtful, of course, whether women gossip more than men, although that is a cliché of our age. Some of the most malicious gossips I have known have been men, and of the people least prone to gossip, many are women.

The tendency to gossip is something to watch in yourself. When gossip raises its ugly head over the neighbor's fence, over a hand of bridge, or in the executive session of a woman's club, then drop it like a hot iron—not on someone's toes but in a box of sand.

On investigation, most gossip turns out to be either plain fancy spurred on by animosity, or a miserable distortion of the facts. Any piece of adverse criticism of anyone, however deserved, had better be turned into an effort to help that person rather than hurt him.

Francis Quacker, in 1620, gave advice that is still good, "Let the greatest part of the news thou hearest be the least part of what thou believest, lest the greatest part of what thou believest be the least part of what is true."

A gossip's real intent is to do a person harm, and in their guerilla warfare of hit, destroy, and run too few gossips suffer sufficiently with the conscience that theirs is a low, frivolous, and dirty business, the bane and disgrace of society. However, gossips are usually suitably decorated with the reputation, even by other gossips, of having empty heads and malicious tongues, and the finer people avoid them.

One of our town gossips and a couple of her cronies had been dissecting everyone they knew, except themselves, with their usual axe and crowbar. They were sitting in a restaurant and the expert paused for momentary lack of another victim and ordered a sandwich and a glass of milk.

"Wouldn't you like the milk in a saucer?" one of the cronies suggested.

A good rule is to talk about things and not about people; if you must talk about people, stick to incontrovertible fact; and play up what is good about them. If there is nothing good to be said about a person, it is by far best to say nothing at all.

If you ever discover that a gossip has been smearing you with calumny, refuse to soil your hands in rebuttal, and give it not even the attention of a worry.

Marcus Aurelius, who was accustomed to having nasty, untrue things said about him as Emperor of Rome, wrote:

"Why should these things people say distract thee? What they say does not change thee; an opinion can hurt a man only if he will think himself wronged. That which men say about him cannot make the man himself the worse, neither can it hurt him inwardly where his nature resides."

Tell whoever brings such gossip to your attention the story of the columnist who was being given some supposedly choice, juicy, but actually worthless, material by a notorious gossip. Pointing to a person a few yards away who was yawning magnificently, he said, "Shh, lower your voice, I think we are being overheard."

● Common Sense in Housekeeping

The mechanics of good *housekeeping*—the job which occupies the greater part of a woman's time and attention—comes as close to being almost a pure exercise in common sense, unadulterated by fancy, as anything in human experience. It is true that any type of artist (and housework is an art as well as a chore) uses creative imagination and draws on ideals, but the drudgery and mechanics of housework decidedly calls for more common sense than creative imagination. In keeping house, a woman will do well to handle her scullery with a great amount of common sense.

Homemaking, it is true, calls for creative imagination and ideals (moderated, of course, by common sense). But *housekeeping* is almost pure common sense.

A common sense rule in housework: "First things first." In housework no one ever gets to the point when there aren't 50 more things that need to be done, or scream to be done, if your philosophy lets them scream, than you have time to do. And if you ever did get them done, the first 25 would be waiting to be done all over again.

Before marriage a young woman possibly entertains the hair-brained ideal that she will always be caught up with her housework and sit leisurely in the midst of a perfectly kept home a considerable share of the time. After about one week she will have learned that such an ideal is just silly delusion.

An ideal a housewife should never form, a goal she should never set (unless she is deliberately intent on making herself eternally miserable), is *ever* getting housework anywhere near the point where she can sit down because there is nothing further to do. A better attitude is to be able to sit down when everything isn't done.

There isn't even the remotest chance that she will ever reach the ideal of having everything perfectly done, and has time at last to drag her exhausted body to a chair with the last ounce of energy at her disposal. How can there be, with dust always and forever dropping out of clean air (where *does* it come from?), with everyone wearing the same shoes indoors that bring in dirt from outdoors, with our modern cuisine as elaborate as it is, with our standards of living as high as they are, with two people or five people in the family changing to clean clothes every day, with everyone invariably leaving the old clothes thrown around, with small boys forever neglecting ears, and small girls neglecting to tidy up their rooms, and husbands neglecting practically everything, just to mention a few of the least important demands on a housewife's time.

To try to reach this ideal will be to work yourself down to the bone and into a permanent state of frustration. An executive of a corporation might reasonably expect to have such an ideal in his affairs, but he wouldn't have the ghost of a chance if he thought he could do it in the more laborious business of housework. A goal of that type in a housewife is simply foolhardiness bordering on lunacy.

A perfectionist in housework, to borrow a phrase from Oscar Wilde's *Reading Gaol*, kills the thing she loves—all her own and her family's good in living. She suffers, and her family suffers, under the eternal possibility that a piece of furniture might get out of place or some dirt may get where it doesn't belong. Life becomes a nightmare of suspended animation for her family and extended animation for her. The results of keeping a perfect house, even if it were possible, are not worth achieving.

Housework is the one place in human living where Benjamin

Franklin's maxim can be overlooked and where there is considerable sense in not doing today what you can put off until tomorrow—for the simple reason that there is still enough to do today. Housework is no place for high sounding maxims or for ultimate ideals of maximum goals.

The common sense attitude and the common sense procedure in housework is to take first things first, setting for yourself a minimum standard rather than a maximum standard of accomplishment.

First things mean first things: feed the family, wash the dishes, make the beds. From there on follow through, still keeping first things first: merely pick up and place things in order if you can't clean that day; clean the obvious spot off the kitchen floor if you haven't time to scrub it; wipe the dust where it shows on the polished table top, if you can't get around to the chair rungs; get a meal without trimmings if other things demand attention. Above all, don't keep tearing up a part of the house every day trying to be a perfect housekeeper.

In trying to keep first things first, remember that getting an hour behind with a meal is worse than getting an hour behind with the dishes; getting three hours behind with the dishes, which is a three-times-a-day job, is worse than getting three hours behind with the beds, which is a once-a-day job; getting a day behind with the beds is worse than getting a day behind with the wash, which is a once-a-week job; getting a week behind with the wash is worse than getting a week behind with washing windows, which is a seasonal job. If you miss a season's housecleaning once in a while, shrug it off. Remember your husband didn't miss it; husbands hate housecleaning about as much as little boys hate washing behind their ears.

It's wonderful and surprising what a lot of things can wait, what a livable home one can keep, if one does first things first, getting around to the other things if, and when, one has time. It's wonderful to sit down once in a while and play a jolly game of peek-a-boo with the bit of dust peeking from behind the piano.

Keeping house on this basis doesn't mean you are slovenly

or that you are lazy. It simply means your life and your house have the order of common sense. If first things are done, a house is livable, even if there's still a trace of dust under the chairs, a basket of wash in the basement, or a closetful of clothes to be aired.

In the evening go to bed content with what has been done, and without a qualm about what hasn't been done, without a thought of crowding into tomorrow what you didn't do today.

That is just common sense devoid of any high ideals.

● Your Ideals for Homemaking Should Be Carefully Selected

Common sense alone does very well in the mechanical aspects of homemaking; that is to say, in the scullery department known as housekeeping.

But the over-all task of *homemaking* requires creative imagination, and creative imagination usually results in establishing ideals of the kind of home you wish to create.

Be careful about ideals. They are not an unmixed blessing. The kind of ideals to have are those that are *ideas for living,* as though the word "ideal" were derived from "idea" + "l" (standing for "living") = an idea for living. In this meaning, an idea is a plan for riding through the difficulties that living imposes, in a way that has been found by experience to be effective, but a flexible plan that can be altered and improved upon as the need arises.

The kind of ideal not to have is the set, static, ultimate-value type of ideal into which you try to warp your living. This type gets people into more trouble than it is worth. Ideals of this kind have a high compulsive value. It is almost impossible for people who have them to give them up. They act as whips that drive people to action, and finally to foolish frustration at having failed. Men who start wars whip people into the spirit of their aims by coupling up with an ideal of this inflexible, compulsive variety.

● Selecting Ideals for Homemaking

1. Choose ideals that stand a reasonable chance of ful-

fillment. Do not choose ideals that are impossibly high and beyond common sense. It would be silly, for instance, for a woman with a low income, and destined to remain in the low income bracket, to have an ideal of living in a style and type of house far above her means.

Many women, before they have experienced married life, have formed ideals of the family they intend to have, including high visions of the kind of house, the kind of husband, the kind of children, and the kind of family living. If these ideals are impossible and too high, and are not changed after marriage, they create the atmosphere for a defeat that grows deeper through the years. Frequently these women, when they reach their 50's and realize how very wide their accomplishment is of the mark they set, develop a reactive depression, a state of complete regret, absolute despair, negation, and futility.

2. Regard an ideal as a standard you would like to attain, and not an all-or-none matter on the attainment of which you are staking all your happiness. Never think of an ideal as something that *must* be realized or all will be lost. Whenever you set up any kind of an ideal in living, it is highly advisable at the same time to make the mental reservation that if you fall short in the attainment of your ideal, your disappointment will be moderate and tempered with the feeling that there are other ideals and values that can be substituted.

3. Pick the kind of ideals that have a running value, a day-to-day value, instead of a value whose attainment is reached only at the end of many years. Or another way of putting it: have ideals that are *ways* of living, rather than ideals that are *ends* in themselves. It is far better to have ideals of the kind of home you can make right now, with what you have, than ideals of the kind of house you hope to have ten years from now with three more children and twice the income.

4. Ideals should never be so fixed that they cannot be altered or replaced in the face of unforeseen conditions. Creative imagination is an adequate substitute for the finest unattainable ideal. A lady I knew set her mind on her only son becoming a chemical engineer like his father. She very nearly crushed him trying to force him through high school, and when he turned out not to be college material, which everyone else had known for years, she met the situation with complete disappointment, frustration, and rejection of her son.

Keeping this mixture of common sense in your choice of ideals for homemaking will materially add to your eventual well-being.

● *Ideals as to the Kind of Place a Home Should Be*

Home is the place where members of the family come for at least two purposes—eating and sleeping.

The best test for the worth of the home is whether its members wish to stay there in preference to any other place open to them.

As Robert Frost put it, "Home is the place where, when you have to go there, they have to take you in." We might add "A good home is the place you prefer to be whether you have to go there or not."

There is more in making the home a magnet for its people than putting in a warm stove.

The biggest single drawing card of the home is the mother in it, just as she may be the force in some homes that induces the others to stay away. A Chinese proverb has it, "A hundred men may make an encampment, but it takes a woman to make a home."

Let us be realistic. The excellence of the physical plant does make a difference. Other things being equal, and up to a certain degree, the more physically appealing and excellent its furnishings, the more a home is a place to which its people like to come. But other things are not always equal, not by any means, and the plain, poorly furnished place is often more preferred by its members, than is the place with elegant appointments. *It is the woman in the place that makes the difference.*

1. Your first ideal is to make the home the kind of place your family wants to stay in above all other places. The determining factors will be what you add to the place, physically and spiritually.

2. Your second ideal is to keep the place orderly and neat. It needn't be spotless and dust-free, except where these might hit one in the eye as a disorder.

It needn't be exquisitely furnished, but the minimum of human comfort and feeling of easy satisfaction that is going to make a person want to stay home, calls for plain, simple orderliness. A perennial pile of dirty, smelly dishes and pans in the kitchen, a stack of yesterday's ironing on the living room table, somebody's nylons eternally drying over the backs of chairs, bottles of tonics and corn cures all over the sideboard, and a flock of untidy children fighting in the general tumult and confusion, will send the husband to a tavern and to drink, or to the country club and to gambling. What easier things are there for him to pursue away from home, except other women.

3. The third ideal is to fix up the house as tastefully as your means will permit. Even on a low budget, a housewife's imagination can do things with a 25-cent can of paint and a yard of colored cloth which for sheer inspiration and ingenuity are the equal of any poem or metal gadget any man ever turned out. No matter how lowly your possessions, with a bit of arranging, a fresh little something here and there, even a small vase of dandelions the first thing in spring—such little twists and touches of artistry can add that pleasant note of appeal for which no one remembers to thank you, about which no one even makes a remark. But everyone accepts it as part of the environment that by its presence makes the home more comfortable, more enjoyable to live in.

An important part of this ideal is to get as much beauty— ritual, if you will, but "graceful living" is the better term — into the home and home life.

See to it that your home life has more dignity and grace than living in a hotel or eating in the Greasy Spoon Restaurant. Pull the family out of the mess and out of the utilitarian spirit of the kitchen. Don't eat in the kitchen if you have a dining room.

About the least you can do as a housewife is to carry the meal to the dining room. Of course it will take more work, you'll use more dishes (I hope), you'll have a more tastefully set table than in the kitchen, you'll serve more neatly, you'll be inclined to cook better and a greater variety, and you'll have to carry everything back to the kitchen (don't leave the salt, sugar, and a pile of dishes on the table). But the additional trouble will more than repay you in the way of the dignity and grace that is added to everyone's living.

And for goodness sakes, don't spoil the table by littering it with every kind of commercial container from milk cartons and peanut butter jars to bottles of catsup. Put up a valiant resistance any time someone leaves the table to go to the cupboard or icebox and comes back with a bottle of catsup or a carton of milk; it either goes into a household container for that sort of thing, or it sits on the floor.

In the new type of small home where the dining area and kitchen are separated only by an imaginary line, the wife must be especially smart and particularly orderly if she is to raise the family meals above a lunch-counter atmosphere to the dignity of good family living.

And as for the food, make it an adventure. A woman with imagination (here is another function of fancy again) can do infinitely more with 75 cents' worth of hamburger than many a restaurant can do with a four-dollar steak.

And last, but far from least, there is yourself. Fix yourself up, too! Fit yourself into the picture of graceful living.

A wonderful elderly housewife I once knew gave her daughter, who also turned out to be a fabulous housekeeper, just *one* simple piece of advice when the daughter was about to be married. It was simply, "Be sure and comb your hair before breakfast." The idea in that remark covers the matter. But let's drive it home a little deeper.

Some way or another, *before the husband and older children get home,* (only you of all human beings will ever know how it is done while you are running to the basement with your arms full of fruit jars and to the attic with your hands full of old junk) you've got to push, wheedle and maneuver that scraggly mop of hair into something suggesting order and resembling beauty; you need to prop up that sagging face with a glow of serenity; you've got to be dressed like your mother was 30 years ago when she went to a party. To carry the whole family idea off successfully, to make it the place your people most like to come, to equip the home for gracious living, *you have to look like something you may not feel like looking,* and you have to act the part, too.

This is what is known to salesmen as putting up a front.

The front you put up, your appearance, is more important in giving the home an air of order, graciousness and plain likability than any other single factor.

The present-day young housewife wisely saves herself a great amount of washing, and also saves on girdles and stockings, by living much of her domestic life in slacks and shirts. It is perfectly possible to be neatly feminine in slacks and shirt, just as it is possible to look like a rag and a bone and a hank of hair by wearing sloppy slippers, dowdy slacks, grimy shirt tails, and a mat of hair anchored to a sullen face by a forest of pin curls.

Femininity is still a power from which women should resist being emancipated. A wife who is habitually slovenly and dowdy is neither a happy thought for a husband nor a pleasant sight to meet. The desire to come home to it, the courage to view it, gradually and slowly weakens.

Old dowdy clothes and a hank of hair may not make a young or an old husband die, but he'll gradually fade away.

4. *A fourth ideal is to provide your home with enough recreational facilities to keep everyone happy.* Some way you've got to turn it into a gymnasium, a bowling alley, a shooting gallery, and just a place to have a high old time all the time. There must not only be games for the children, but you must show them how to play. There should be things for the whole family to do together, activities devised by you, initiated by you, led by you. It must be something that will include your husband: cribbage, bridge, euchre, or a football game board in winter, a croquet or badminton court in summer. Whether you live in an apartment or not, there should be picnics, out-

ings, excursions, entertainments, inviting people in, going out. Don't interfere with your husband's hobbies. Be glad he has one.

5. A fifth ideal is to spend no more money on yourself and the family than you can afford. Macawbre in Dicken's *David Copperfield* sagely put it thus:

"Annual income twenty pounds, annual expenditure nineteen six, result: happiness . . .

"Annual income twenty pounds, annual expenditure twenty pounds nought and six, result: misery."

Financing a home on a small margin is just one of the hundred capacities a woman has to have to be a successful homemaker. She has to keep the whole family clothed, fed, the house acceptably furnished on a budget that would make a purchasing agent in any business scream with rage. She must be an efficiency expert, a Bureau of Standards buying expert, and a smart and astute financier to do it.

To preserve her feeling of well-being, to keep her head out of a noose of trouble, she must never, never buy what she cannot afford, even if she goes without a suitable spring coat and the living room goes without a new rug. There is no easier way to make oneself miserable, or to enrage a husband, than to operate the family budget in the red.[1]

How the average family today can maintain the standard of living it does, on the income it does, is a matter of which the average man, if he is truthful, has no adequate idea or appreciation. It is another of woman's accomplishments that is in the order of a miracle. But there is nothing of the order of a miracle in the life of the woman who constantly spends what she does not have; nor in the life of her husband.

Today 26 per cent of all married women have a job outside the home. This fact is an indication of woman's emancipation, of the family need for a higher income to maintain a certain

---

[1] Excellent advice on handling marital finances will be found in *Building a Successful Marriage;* Landis, Judson T. and Mary G. Landis, Prentice-Hall, Inc., 1953. Chapter XVI—Finances and Adjustment in Marriage, p. 330 ff. Chapter XVII—Getting Your Money's Worth, p. 341 ff. Chapter XVIII—Buying Life Insurance, p. 354 ff. Chapter XIX—Family Planning, p. 375 ff.

standard of living, and of many women's disgust and boredom with housework.

There are no good rules to govern the decision of whether a married woman should have an occupation or career outside the home. Each individual case involves too many factors to allow for much generalization.

If she has childen, it will be hard for her to take an outside job without some degree of help at home, and getting help at home is a problem nowadays.

A capable woman can manage full time work outside the home and still do a good job rearing the children. But it will be harder, especially harder on her, and the chances of failure are greater. The average woman with a family will do better for herself and for her children to accept homemaking as a full-time occupation until the children are in their upper teens.

- *Ideals to Entertain, and Not to Entertain, About a Husband*

In our kind of society, a woman who wants a home and a family must, of course, have a husband, even though some husbands can be more trouble than trying to raise a family without one.

Whatever you plan on doing, entertain no illusions or impossible ideals concerning a husband. Husbands are frequently ideal-shattering creatures. If you want to be happily married, never place your husband under the onus of living up to an ideal.

The choice of a husband. Before marriage, you may if you wish, *picture* what a husband is going to be like. But be sure to picture the lower extreme as well as the higher. Then try to picture the husband you can reasonably expect.

In looking around for one, look around for the reasonable one.

In practise, selecting a husband is not as great a problem as it appears to be on paper. There are exceedingly few women who are privileged to select a husband from 10, 25, 50 or a hundred different men, and it is surprising how often those who have so wide a choice come up with a lemon instead of a ripe, luscious plum. Too often we blame the partner for failure. It is obvious from the repeaters that some people cannot get along any better with one person than with another; they could not get along with anyone. It is just as obvious that some people could make a success of it with almost anybody.

Be a husband ever so terrible, a capable woman will succeed in making him a little less so and manage to round out a life with him.

For most women, picking a husband is in the same category as voting for President. There are only two or three candidates; between the candidates there is neither much difference nor much choice; with either of them the future is fairly unpredictable. After being in a quandary, she finally votes for one or the other; and in the end she puts up with the one she gets. Thus there is at least this one similarity her husband has with the President of the United States, a thought she can always pull out of the bag and admire should all his other qualities turn out poorly.

The ideal picture of a husband would be one who is utterly handsome, perfectly unselfish, with a warm, pleasant, steady disposition; a perfect lover; understanding of all others and able to make himself understandable; one who loves children and who loves you (but not other women); who is kindly, thoughtful, and agreeable at all times; who is delightfully but not objectionably witty and brilliant, talks well but not too much. He is ambitious and capable in his work, with a wonderfully successful career that is financially bountiful, and which leaves plenty of time for him to help you and to entertain you and the children. He is crazy, of course, about housework, even insists on doing the washing and ironing. He is tidy and clean, puts his clothes and shoes away, tells no dirty stories, and has no fetishes, disagreeable manners or irksome idiosyncracies. He knows how to eat cherries with seeds, is not finicky in his eating or in anything else, entertains no impossible expectations of you, has no halitosis nor body odor, and is never sick.

The minimum picture of a husband would be a creature having no qualities other than being a man—hardly even a man

—devoid of every quality ever deemed advisable in a human being, and possessed with all the bad ones.

A reasonable picture of a husband is one who is as lovable for what he isn't as for what he is; one who can earn a living on an acceptable standard, is fairly agreeable and no more than occasionally quarrelsome. He is fairly understanding, reasonably free from obnoxious habits such as drinking, gambling, and household laziness, reasonably affectionate, and fairly good to you and the family. He is truthful in the main, on the whole loyal, and he tries to be helpful even if he isn't always too thoughtful.

11 ≫

The Factual Basis of Marriage

● *The Facts on Which to Plan Your Marriage*

How happy can you reasonably expect your own marriage to be?

What characteristics in husbands and wives make for success and failure in marriage?

Sociologists, psychologists, and marriage counselors have accumulated a great fund of facts and helpful information on these points that every woman should know. To get this information would require considerable reading. So we summarize it in this chapter as concisely as possible and in as detailed a way as you need to have it.

1. Marriage is not a continuous heaven of happiness. Do not be discouraged if as early as the first few weeks you discover that marriage is not continual bliss. Hardly any marriage is. In the average marriage there is a great, great amount of the commonplace, and a relatively small amount of high ecstacy. Every marriage, even the very successful ones, have periods of strain and stress. When things do not seem to be going well the husband or the wife needs to use a bit more common sense to make things go better again.

2. A successful relation between a husband and wife requires many attitudes, as well as many capacities on the part of both. Success in marriage is not a guarantee conferred

178

by the final words of the wedding ceremony. What comes out of marriage depends on what goes into it. The marriage will be as good as the combined qualities of the two people can make it. How good it will be will depend very largely on their attitudes, preferences, aversions, habit patterns, and prejudices, all of which can be summed up under the single term of maturity. Two immature people have very little chance of a successful marriage. One very mature person can build a happy life even with someone fairly immature, but it will not be an easy accomplishment. Two people, both mature in the attitudes described in this book, will certainly be happy.

No attitude is more necessary than the realization that the two sexes are mutually complementary, neither is born to be dominated or to dominate, neither is inherently superior or inferior, both have different potentials and make their special contribution to human living. A successful relationship depends on the cooperative use of their complementary talents, not on dominance and subservience.

3. People marry in order to satisfy many different needs— sexual, economic, social, the desire for a family—and because society is organized for married people. But the most important reasons for getting married, conscious or unconscious, are personality needs. The following table lists the personal needs which 373 men and women, who had been married less than a year, hoped to have satisfied by their marriage: [1]

It should be noted that the things men and women desire from marriage do not differ greatly, but while both sexes have the same needs, women are more conscious of their needs. This is indicated by the fact that 11 of the 15 items were more highly desired by women.

The happy marriages are those in which both husband and wife find fulfillment of a majority of these needs. How fully they can accomplish this will depend on their respective maturities.

4. Those who fail in marriage are the immature. They

---

[1] E. W. Burgess, and H. J. Locke, *The Family*, Second Edition (New York: American Book Company, 1953) p. 420.

Table 2

PERCENTAGES OF 373 MEN AND WOMEN STATING VARIOUS
PERSONALITY NEEDS WHICH THEY HOPED TO HAVE SATISFIED
THROUGH MARRIAGE

Personality Need	Men	Women
Someone to love me	36.4%	53.5%
Someone to confide in	30.6	40.0
Someone to show affection	20.8	30.0
Someone to respect my ideals	26.0	26.0
Someone to appreciate what I wish to achieve	28.3	24.0
Someone to understand my moods	23.1	27.5
Someone to help make my decisions	15.0	32.5
Someone to stimulate my ambition	26.6	21.0
Someone to look up to	16.2	29.0
Someone to give me self-confidence	19.6	24.0
Someone to back me in difficulty	16.2	25.5
Someone to appreciate me just as I am	20.2	20.5
Someone to admire my ability	18.5	19.5
Someone to make me feel important	20.8	17.0
Someone to relieve my loneliness	18.5	18.5

can be characterized in general as impulsive and lacking self-mastery; they are tense, nervous, irritable, gloomy, uncoöperative, tending to take little interest in people as a whole, or in community affairs, given to nagging, whining, complaining, and fault finding.[2]

The women who fail in marriage have the following general personality characteristics: [3]

1. Are characterized by emotional tenseness.

2. Inclined toward ups and downs of moods.

3. Give evidence of deep-seated inferiority feelings to which they react by aggressive attitudes rather than by timidity.

[2] J. T. Landis, and M. G. Landis, Building a Successful Marriage, (Englewood Cliffs, N. J.: Prentice-Hall, Inc., 1953), p. 93.
[3] ibid, p. 90-91. Landis and Landis so summarized material contained in L. M. Terman, Psychological Factors in Marital Happiness, (New York: McGraw-Hill Book Co., 1938), pp. 142-166.

4. Are inclined to be irritable and dictatorial.

5. Have compensatory mechanisms resulting in restive striving, as evidenced by becoming active joiners, aggressive in business, and over-anxious in social life.

6. Strive for wide circle of acquaintances; are more concerned with being important than being liked.

7. Are egocentric.

8. Have little interest in benevolent and welfare activities unless these activities offer personal recognition.

9. Like activities fraught with opportunities for romance.

10. Are more inclined to be conciliatory in attitudes toward men than toward women.

11. Are impatient and fitful workers.

12. Dislike cautious or methodical people.

13. Dislike types of work that require methodical and painstaking effort.

14. In politics, religion, and social ethics are more often radical.

The men who fail show personality characteristics comparable, although not exactly the same:

1. Are inclined to be moody and somewhat neurotic.

2. Are prone to feelings of social inferiority.

3. Dislike being conspicuous in public.

4. Are highly reactive to social opinion.

5. Often compensate for a sense of social insecurity by domineering attitudes.

6. Take pleasure in commanding roles over business dependents or women.

7. Withdraw from playing inferior role or competing with superiors.

8. Often compensate by daydreams and power fantasies.

9. Are sporadic and irregular in their habits of work.

10. Dislike detail and methodical attitude.

11. Dislike saving money.

12. Like to wager.

13. More often express irreligious attitudes.

14. More inclined to radicalism in sex morals and politics.

Table 3

Order for Husbands	Order for Wives
1. W. nags me	1. H. selfish and inconsiderate
2. W. not affectionate	2. H. unsuccessful in business
3. W. selfish and inconsiderate	3. H. is untruthful
4. W. complains too much	4. H. complains too much
5. W. interferes with hobbies	5. H. does not show affection
6. W. slovenly in appearance	6. H. does not talk things over
7. W. is quick-tempered	7. H. harsh with children
8. W. interferes with my discipline	8. H. touchy
9. W. conceited	9. H. has no interest in children
10. W is insincere	10. H. not interested in home
11. W.'s feelings too easily hurt	11. H. not affectionate
12. W. criticizes me	12. H. rude
13. W. narrow-minded	13. H. lacks ambition
14. W. neglects the children	14. H. nervous or impatient
15. W. a poor housekeeper	15. H. criticizes me
16. W. argumentative	16. H.'s poor management of income
17. W. has annoying habits	17. H. narrow-minded
18. W. untruthful	18. H. not faithful to me
19. W. interferes in my business	19. H. lazy
20. W. spoils the children	20. H. bored with my small talk
21. W.'s poor management of income	21. In-laws
22. In-laws	22. H. easily influenced by others
23. Insufficient income	23. H. tight with money
24. W. nervous or emotional	24. H. argumentative
25. W. easily influenced by others	25. H.'s insufficient income
26. W. jealous	26. H. has no backbone

Order for Husbands	Order for Wives
27. W. lazy	27. H. dislikes to go out with me
28. W. gossips indiscreetly	28. H. pays attention to other women

5. The most serious problems encountered in the marriages of 818 people, listed in their order of frequency were concerned with these factors: economic, sex, in-law adjustment, bad temper, intolerance, selfishness, lack of consideration, impatience, and moodiness.[4]

The common grievances against their wives which another group of 792 husbands listed, and the grievances against their husbands of 792 wives, are listed in Table 3, in descending order with the most common complaint first.[5]

6. Sexual relations are important in making a marriage a success or a failure. But many authorities are agreed that the sexual element is far from being the most important factor.[6] A marriage can be happy and a success where sexual adjustment is never reached, even when, as with one of my patients, the sexual act was never consummated during 55 years of happy marriage.

Similarly, marriages can be failures and end in divorce even when sexual adjustment is highly satisfactory. Sexual conflict is often merely the indication of a deeper personality conflict. Sexual incompatibility is apt to be a part of a general selfishness and inability to cooperate. Only 65 per cent of couples happily married for 20 years considered their sex relations mutually satisfactory.[7]

---

[4] *Ibid.,* p. 96.
[5] L. M. Terman, *op. cit.,* p. 99.
[6] L. M. Terman, opicit., p. 247.
    Landis and Landis, opicit., p. 281.
    E. W. Burgess, and L. S. Cottrell, *Predicting Success or Failure in Marriage,* (Englewood Cliffs, N. J.: Prentice-Hall, Inc., 1939), Chapter 12, "The Sexual Factor."
    A. G. Truxal, and F. E. Merrill, *Marriage and the Family in American Culture,* (Englewood Cliffs, N. J.: Prentice-Hall, Inc., 1953), p. 258.
[7] Landis and Landis, *op. cit.* 261.

7. The chances of being happy or unhappy in marriage are approximately these:[8]

Happy or very happy .... 63.0 per cent

Happy or very unhappy .... 22.0 per cent

In between .... 14.0 per cent

The divorce possibility in marriage today is one for every three and a half marriages, and the trend is still upward. Divorce takes place more often in the third and fourth years, and two-thirds of all divorces materialize in the first nine years. Divorces are more common with short engagements than with long engagements; more common when men marry before the age of 20 and women before the age of 18, more common among childless couples, among unskilled laborers, among urban people, and when one or both partners come from homes broken by divorce or from homes in which there was much friction and unhappy parents.

8. Women who make a success of their marriage tend to have these characteristics: [9]

1. Have kindly attitudes toward others.

2. Expect kindly attitudes from others.

3. Do not easily take offense.

4. Not unduly concerned about the impressions they make upon others.

5. Do not look upon social relationships as rivalry situations.

6. Are cooperative.

7. Do not object to subordinate roles.

8. Are not annoyed by advice from others.

9. Frequently have missionary and ministering attitudes.

10. Enjoy activities that bring educational and pleasurable opportunities to others.

11. Like to do things for the dependent or underprivileged.

12. Are methodical and painstaking in their work.

13. Are careful in regard to money.

14. In religion, morals, and politics tend to be conservative and conventional.

---

[8] Burgess and Cottrell, *op. cit.*, pp. 34 and 139.

[9] Summarized by Landis and Landis, *op. cit.*, pp. 90-91, from material presented by Terman, *op. cit.*, pp. 142-166.

Table 4

Rank Order for Husbands	Rank Order for Wives
Affection	Affection
Understanding	Mutual interests
Give and take	Cooperation
Cooperation	Give and take
Children	Understanding
Mutual interests	Talking things over
Religion	Religion
Tolerance	Desire for success
Desire for success	Respect
Well acquainted before marriage	Children
Hard work	Tolerance
No financial problems	Similar backgrounds
Talking things over	Consideration
Patience	Even temper
Respect	Well acquainted before marriage
Common sense	Old enough to marry
Trust	No financial problems
Faith	Common sense
Holding temper	Faith
Similar backgrounds	Hard work
Consideration	Holding temper
Old enough to marry	Compromise
Honest	Sense of humor
Compromise	Honesty
Sense of humor	Patience

15. Have expressed attitudes that imply a quiet self-assurance and a decidedly optimistic outlook upon life.

The husbands who were successfully married had very similar characteristics:

1. Have even and stable emotional tone.

2. Are cooperative.

3. Show attitude toward women that reflects equalitarian ideals.

4. Have benevolent attitude toward inferiors and the underprivileged.

5. Tend to be unselfconscious and somewhat extroverted.

6. Show superior initiative.
7. Have a greater tendency to take responsibility.
8. Show greater willingness to give close attention to detail.
9. Like methodical procedures and methodical people.
10. Are saving and cautious in money matters.
11. Hold conservative attitudes.
12. Have a favorable attitude toward religion.
13. Strongly uphold the sex mores and other social conventions.

Several hundred husbands and wives who had been happily married for an average of 20 years listed the following factors as making for success in marriage. They are listed in Table 4 in the order of importance given them by either sex.[10]

9. Marriage failure can be traced to three causes in the large proportion of cases: [11]

Inflexible, rigid personalities; people unable to change themselves in order to meet the many marriage situations that require new ways, outlooks and reactions. Such pepole cannot "give in" in arguments, are quick to anger, dominating, selfish.[12]

Inability to understand and give consideration to others (unable to *identify* themselves with others) to put themselves in the other people's place and feel as they feel, an ability constantly required of each spouse in the marriage relationship.[13]

Inability either to see problems or think them through; they have no positive program for meeting problems. They cannot see problems clearly, or, if they can, they cannot face them realistically and seek intelligent solutions. They live at a little distance from fact in a mild fantasy state and cannot come to grips with reality.[14]

10. Quarrels over tremendous trifles are the inevitable result of the three immaturities mentioned above. Many needless quarrels arise because of pent-up emotional tensions

---

10 Landis and Landis, *op. cit.*, p. 100.
11 Landis and Landis, *op. cit.*, p. 100.
12 Immaturity No. 5, Chapter X.
13 Immaturity No. 3, Chapter VII.
14 Immaturity No. 8, Chapter XIII.

which the husband brings home from conflict situation in his work. When he comes home he relaxes his self-restraint and gives expression to his frustrations and tensions by flaring up over some tremendous trifle. If his wife could understand the underlying psychological mechanism, she might see that by acting as his sparring partner she fulfills one of her marital functions by absorbing his emotional unbalance. Unfortunatety, few wives can take that attitude, and quarreling of this kind simply builds up new tensions and contributes more trouble.

The happily married couple curbs the impulse to say bitter words, or the cutting retort; they withhold scathing criticism in order to avoid unpleasantness and try to minimize their disagreements.

This is one of the primary requirements in marriage.

11. The family conference method of settling problems is a good one, but it must be started early in marriage. Preferably it should be decided even before marriage that they will talk over differences that are bound to arise.

Men find it much more difficult to adopt the conference method of settling differences. The man's reluctance is partly a relic from former generations when it was man's prerogative to make all the decisions and woman's place to accept them, and partly that he senses his wife is right in most disagreements and keener in presenting her point of view. This has been turned defensively into the cliché, "Once you let your wife get talking, you won't be able to get a word in edgewise." In Table 4 the wives consider talking things over much more important to their happiness than men do. The wife usually resents a husband's failure to talk. Wives feel that a husband's unwillingness to confer on differences means that either he does not think the differences important, or that he is determined not to change his viewpoint. Even if the husband tries to solve the difficulties by saying "yes" and giving in without a quarrel, the wife never finds him of any help in working out problems of other kinds, such as the problems involving the children.

TABLE 5

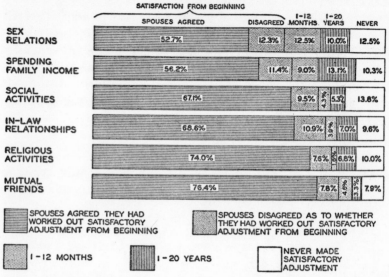

Percentage of 818 spouses reporting various periods of time required after marriage to achieve adjustment in six areas. People who had been successfully married for an average of 20 years had experienced greater difficulty in adjusting in certain areas. From Judson T. Landis, "Length of Time Required to Achieve Adjustment in Marriage," *American Sociological Review*, 11:6 (December, 1946), 668.

Unless such conferences are instituted early, it is a rare husband who could be induced to start them later in marriage.

12. Little change should be expected after marriage. Never count on changing a man after marriage. Most people find it hard to admit weaknesses and faults. Criticisms puncture their egos, and they react either by withdrawl or by counter measures. Wanting to be loved for himself, faults and all, was probably one reason he married a person who seemed, at one time, to love him, faults and all.

Certain rare individuals are mature enough to welcome constructive criticism from the spouse. But it is much safer and less likely to lead to disappointment if both members proceed on the assumption that the partners will do little changing after marriage.

13. Marital adjustments require a little time. A married couple should not regard as failure their inability to adjust on all matters immediately or even very soon. For only about half of married couples are sex relations satisfactory from the beginning. For 12.5 per cent of couples sex adjustment required a year and in another 10 per cent 20 years were necessary.

The best available data on the time it takes to adjust to the important factors in marriage is shown in the graph in Table 5, taken from Landis.[15]

It will be noted that more time was required for adjusting in sex relations and in spending the family income than in the other parts of living together.

● Above All: Put a Rich Mixture of Common Sense into Your Ideals

To approach marriage with a pattern of ideals into which you are going to force a husband and children is to run a good chance of ending up defeated and frustrated.

A much sounder procedure, by far, is to plan bringing to your marriage, within yourself, as many of the maturities as you can possibly muster. Dealing with your responsibilities in a mature way will help even a relatively immature husband in meeting his. There is always a chance that some of your maturity may pass over to him through "social osmosis," in the process of being closely associated.

As you learn to understand your husband better, do not get upset because he does not conform to an ideal you had formed of him, or an ideal you had formed of husbands in general. Accept him as he is on a factual basis. Is he gentle? Does he have a streak of cruelty that bursts out occasionally? Is he inconsiderate at times? Is he apt to neglect little things like paying the bills, kissing you when he comes home, remembering your anniversary? How selfish is he? How neat and clean? Does he get along with people? Is he critical?

Don't *you* be critical. Accept the fact that he is what he is, and rise above it, compensating for his deficiencies by your own maturity. Remember you have a few faults of your own which may be as apparent to him as his are to you. You can do more about your own than you can about his.

---

[15] Landis and Landis, *op. cit.*, p. 259.

12

Making Sex a Happy Part of Life

Arriving at a mature attitude is the total process of arriving at a correct perspective of ourselves in the kind of world we are in.

The mature attitude itself is the general plan for action that will do us the most good within the pattern of that perspective.

If we keep those two definitive points in mind, it will not be difficult to form a mature attitude for dealing with the complicated matter of sex.

This is a subject that is complicated by social tabus and regulations, by all sorts of haphazard and unskilled conditionings in our youth, complicated by psychological and biological differences between man and woman in sexual outlooks and in excitement and response, and complicated finally by living with a husband whose conditionings and requirements are different from your own.

All this obviously cannot be covered exhaustively in a single chapter, which is probably just as well. We can focus on the kernel and disregard the chaff. We can hope to put the perspective into the clear relief of a few lines, and then, just as succinctly, delineate the mature attitude that will serve us "the general plan for action that will do us the most good" within the pattern of that perspective.

Every single one of the other maturities a woman can put into practice *as an individual* in her own private life by, and for,

190

herself. For instance, honesty, enlightened selfishness, making the most of it, self-reliance, a pleasant disposition, are all attitudes she can fulfill by herself. But the ability to make sex a happy part of life is a maturity in which man and woman share a mutual creative responsibility in a way that is true of none of the other maturities. For a woman to achieve the benefits of this maturity requires at least a fair share of a similar maturity in the person chosen for a sexual partner. It thus has a unique quality none of the other maturities have.

This chapter is written neither from the point of view of a woman nor of a man. Therefore, if you think your marital life might be enriched, have your husband read it. It is written from his point of view as much as from yours.

● Premarital Sex Conditioning in Perspective

Many men and women come to the altar with immature sex conditionings that interfere with achieving a happy, mature sex life in marriage.

These conditionings are the result of attitudes and misinformation taught by parents or supplied by schoolmates, or they may be conditioned by unpleasant episodes in early childhood or adolescence.

1. The conditioned idea that sex is dirty, sordid, and wrong. The general impression conveyed to many children through the few hesitant remarks parents make about sex in a disciplinary and cautioning way, is that everything about sex in dirty, sordid, and wrong. Girls are often indoctrinated with this idea more strongly than boys, since girls receive much more family instruction in the tabus than do boys.

2. The misconception of the woman's passive role. Many mothers teach their daughters, by inference as often as openly, that a woman's role in sex should be entirely passive, that sexual intercourse is merely a submission for the wife, indulged in solely for the husband's enjoyment; that it is actually immoral for a woman to enjoy coitus, and doubly immoral to show the husband she enjoys it, or ever to show her desire by making the initial move.

Some boys, although much less often, have this conception too.

Howard, a newly married husband, was highly distraught by his wife Jane's enthusiastic sexual response. He had been taught by his religious parents that only immoral women ever find sexual intimacy enjoyable, and he vigorously accused poor Jane of promiscuous premarital relations, which was entirely untrue. At the end of a few months they would have been ready to separate had not a physician straightened out Howard's misconception by showing him that it was he, and not Jane, who was acting abnormally and immorally.

3. Conditioning girls that sex is painful and unpleasant. Many girls are conditioned to associate all sex matters with pain. They have been severely punished for childhood infractions of sex tabus. They are assured, in preparation for menstruation, that menstruation is usually a painful time of sickness. They have heard tales about the pains of childbirth. They hear the complaints of a nervous mother in the menopause. The mother may tell them that sexual intercouse is painful.

Finally their conditionings are strongly reinforced by the not unusual experience of pain during the honeymoon; pain caused by an immature husband who is more enthusiastic than understanding, more intent on his own pleasure than on sympathetic affection for her.

4. Conditioning fears that sex is dangerous. Some parents try to solve the practical problem of protecting the daughter by planting vague but dreadful fears of men and of any kind of sex activity.

A more extreme case of conditioning of this kind than is ordinarily met with is illustrated by Juanita.

After being married a year, Juanita and her husband were ready to break off their marriage because Juanita had not permitted her husband to make a single sexual entry. The year had been a frightful emotional experience for them both, and Juanita had developed a nonspecific ulcerative colitis because of it.

Because Juanita was an unusually beautiful child and lived in a truly dangerous part of the city, her mother had thoroughly frightened her about every aspect of sex.

5. Conditioned reluctance to discuss sexual difficulties. The attitude in families and in society that never allow sexual matters to be discussed, leads to timidity and reluctance on the part of the wife and husband to discuss any troubles and difficulties they are having in their sexual life. Consequently difficulties, antagonisms, and resentments increase until they constitute a threat to their marital relation.

6. Conditionings in the man. Premarital conditioning in men is somewhat different than in women, but equally conducive to an immature marital adjustment.

Most men grow up to think of sexual intercourse largely as a matter of high enjoyment, and marriage as a nightly spree of sexual indulgence. They have no inkling of an idea that it might be otherwise for the wife, or that it can be on a more meaningful level for them.

When the man has had premarital sexual relations it has usually been with some promiscuous female who had "been there" many times before. When he marries he is disappointed with his wife's responses and is critical of her "frigidity" and lack of response.

7. Correcting the perspective. The facts to correct the wrong perspective of these conditionings are the following:

Sexual intimacy is neither dirty, sordid, nor wrong unless it occurs under sordid, wrong circumstances. The sexual intimacy of two people who have a genuine affection and deep love for each other is one of life's most meaningful and beautiful experiences, and one that adds an additional bond of unity to their marital union.

The woman's sex role is not meant to be passive, any more than her role in life is. It is as active, allows for as much expression, freedom, and initiative, as the man's.

For some women sexual intercourse may be painful at first, and for an indefinite time. Gentleness, sympathetic consideration, and restraint is necessary in the husband if she is not to be conditioned by painful experience to sexual reluctance all through marriage.

Enlightened selfishness on the part of the man will tell him that he can achieve high sexual enjoyment in marriage only if his wife can. It is to his interest to modify his immediate desires in the direction of her satisfaction.

The average man desires coitus more frequently than does the average woman, and too frequent intercourse may become very distasteful to a woman. A man, also, can enjoy coitus under almost any circumstances, even after he and his wife have been quarreling, but his wife cannot submit to intercourse when everything has been going badly between them. Her sexual desire requires a background of affection, companionship, and love.

● *A Perspective of Man's and Woman's Differences in Sexual Response*

About half the men and women find, after they have been married a few months, or even a few years, that their sexual relations are not as they had expected them to be.

They feel that something is wrong with the spouse (never with themselves), that their sexual life is not developing properly, and that unless it does, their marriage may be broken up. They are both dissatisfied and discouraged.

But they need not feel discouraged nor dissatisfied.

The fact is that their unsatisfactory sexual experience is the *usual* experience of one-half of all newly married couples.

The type of thing they are calling an abnormal sex reaction in the spouse is, if they only knew it, a perfectly normal and expected reaction.

It is part of a mature perspective to appreciate that there are differences between a man's and a woman's sexual needs, ease of sexual arousal, circumstances of arousal, and reactions during intercourse. And most important of all, there is a vast difference between the meaning and interpretation a woman places on sexual love, and the interpretation the man gives it.

The main differences to include in the mature perspective are these:

1. Fundamental differences in sexual outlooks. The man's sexual outlook is much more simple and direct, *much more physical,* than is the woman's. The average man is physically aroused by the mere nearness of any female who is attractive to him. It requires nothing more than such nearness to awaken his sexual desires and stimulate his reproductive organs.

It is important for the woman to know that a man's primary sexual feeling is a *physical* one, and that such a feeling is *normal* in a man.

Furthermore, a man's approach is direct. When his sexual desires are aroused his tendency is to proceed directly to a satisfaction of his wants, without more display of affection than he thinks necessary to gain his end, without preliminary whisperings of love or preliminary caressing, and without much considerate feeling for his partner. In actual intercourse he brings on his orgasm as quickly as possible, following which, his needs requited, he is tired and no longer inclined to tenderness or to any show of affection.

Such is the *normal* response in the man, and it continues to be his normal response, until he learns differently.

If the woman knows this and expects it, she will save herself much disappointment and needless worry.

As Dr. Anna K. Daniels says in her excellent book, *It Is Never Too Late to Love:*[1]

> There is no reason for a woman to regard a man as a "beast" simply because he desires to have sexual relations with her. Yet how many women patients come to me and cry, "My husband is a beast! The minute he sees me he wants to rush me off to bed!"
>
> My invariable reply to that complaint is, "You should be flattered and delighted he feels that way about you. If you want to be happy, see to it that he never loses that feeling."

This general picture of the male's sexual outlook would be

---

[1] Englewood Cliffs, N. J.: Prentice-Hall, Inc., 1953.

sadly incomplete if it were left this simple. It needs to be prefaced with the acknowledgement that many men have a sexual maturity to a degree where they bring a precious spiritual component to their love-making.

There is at least a little bit of this conditioning in most men, and the mature wife will be able to nurse it into a splendid, wholesome feeling between them.

In most men there is the subconscious feeling that their bride is not merely a wife, but also a mother, a conditioning that goes back to his boyhood between the years of four to six. Freud termed these the Oedipus complex years, after Oedipus who loved and married the woman whom he did not know was his mother. Most boys of four to six wish to marry their mother, not in a sexual way, which is beyond their true comprehension, but in an affectionate way.

When he marries, this conditioning becomes apparent in his feeling toward his wife.

To most grooms the womanhood of his wife has almost a sacred quality. He views her in the double halo of a mystic mother-wife. She arouses his finest sensitivity, tenderness, and awareness of the things which are precious. She rings every bell there is in him, she turns on all the lights he has. If he could write poetry, he would. If he were a musician, he would compose his masterpiece.

She can destroy and lose this fine feeling in him by being unsympathetic, unmotherly, and on the defensive in her own sexual response, an error so easy for a bride to slip into because she is often a bit dubious about its pleasures, or about how to act.

On the other hand she can preserve her husband's attitude toward her and develop it as the years go by into a truly fine interdependence and companionship.

The bride does not need to worry about how to act. She needs only to remember to be as much mother as wife. Even if in the first marriage days her sexual response cannot be enthusiastic, her motherly attitude and concern for him during the first sexual experimentation must be warm and enthusiastic. She must make him feel that he is wanted, that he is worthy, that he will always be able to come to her and find the mother whom he needs as much as the wife.

The wife, even less in sexual matters than in any others, does not indicate that she knows more than he does. It would be a sad blow to his ego, and to their relationship, if she tried overtly to instruct him in what to do, how to respond to her, and how to get her to respond to him. She has a better method of instruction at her disposal, which is to *show* her genuine pleasure when he does something well. She is a mother whose method of discipline is warm approval rather than cold disapproval.

She must never indicate, by word or act, that his sexual love is of no interest to her, that she "could easily do without ever having it." He wishes above all to merit her appreciation; he is pleased when she is pleased.

The women's sexual outlook is much less physical, and is much more tempered by spiritual love. To respond physically she must feel an existing oneness that is both a deep friendship and a deep affection; she regards the act of coitus as the embodiment of that affection, that spiritual love, and that oneness, and not merely the physical relief of a physical desire. She cannot accept intercourse as lightly as can a man. To her it is more meaningful than a passing whim. She is ready less often than a man, nor can she come to it with as little preparation as can a man. The woman must generally be built up to intercourse. She must practically be wooed every time. What her husband's attitude has been during the day, has much to do with her receptivity; her husband's affection needs to be apparent; she needs to be petted, embraced, kissed, and caressed. General fatigue affects her response very much more, and during the busy child-rearing years she is not always able to meet her husband as enthusiastically as he would like. Even the general tenor of her day has much to do with her sexual mood. As one husband remarked (more discerningly than he realized), "My wife will have intercourse only when everything has gone well during the day."

It is important for the man to know that this characteristic reaction is *normal* in a woman.

These differences in the sexual outlook of men and women are partly cultural but also partly biological. The entire sex act is over in a few minutes for a man, but it lasts nine months and at least another year for the woman. One cannot expect her to take it nonchalantly.

2. *Fundamental differences in frequency of sexual desire.* We have already said that the average man desires sexual intercourse more frequently than does a woman.

This difference is not as constant as the one we have just noted concerning the general sexual outlook. We doctors quite often see husbands with considerably less desire for coitus than their wives, and while this need not be regarded as abnormal, yet it is less frequently found than the reverse.

If the couple is mature, the frequency with which they have sexual intercourse will be a compromise. If he is selfish and demanding, it will probably be a nightly occurrence; and the wife will be unhappy with the turn their sexual life has taken. If it is she who is selfish, intercourse may be infrequent, and he is the one who will be dissatisfied.

In this matter both partners must be mature enough to cooperate and to compromise.

There is no number that one can give as being the normal frequency of coitus in marriage. Whatever a cooperative couple finds will best satisfy both their needs is normal for that couple. Investigations on the matter, such as the Kinsey report, all show about the same thing. Most young couples of 20 to 30 average two or three times a week. This number gradually decreases until at 55 to 60 it is once every one or two weeks. But the variations are so wide and so numerous that an average does not mean a great deal.

On a night when she does not feel up to it, the wife should not put her husband off sourly nor perfunctorily. Nor should she have the attitude, "Go ahead, it never means anything to me anyway."

It is far better for her to explain to her husband in the warmly sympathetic manner of a mother with a child, that she cannot respond as often as he, that he must be content in her affection until she can again respond warmly and with the enthusiasm that delights him. Once he understands, he will be satisfied and delighted with her affection. On the other hand, a cold repulse without explanation will hurt him, make him dejected, and somewhat hostile.

3. Fundamental differences of sexual response. Just as a woman is slower in her sexual arousal than a man, so she is slower in achieving an orgasm.

An orgasm is less tiring and wearing in a woman than in a man, even though hers lasts longer.

Achieving a climax is impossible for most women in the absence of the strong spiritual certainty that she has the affection and deep love of her partner. The man reaches a climax through physical friction alone, regardless of any spiritual component. But not the woman. For her to realize a climax she must have (1) built up in herself the physical need for sexual release, (2) she must feel that a spiritual oneness exists with the mate, and (3) the husband's climax must be delayed long enough for her to build up to hers. The absence of any one of these three factors accounts for the large number of women who seldom or never reach a climax in intercourse. It is desirable that she does not reach a climax at least some of the time; it provides emotional relief and adds to the richness of the sexual life.

A man can have a climax with any woman.

The woman who never has a climax simply has never been loved by the right man, in the right way, at the right time. As Dr. Anna K. Daniels puts it, "There is no woman so frigid that a good man cannot defrost her."[2]

It is less important to the woman that she reach a climax than it is to the man that he has one, or that she has one. The man is deeply unhappy unless he does, except under the one condition given below. But the woman can enjoy suitable pleasure in intercourse even in its absence.

---

[2] *Op. cit.*, p. 159.

There is one interesting situation where a man likewise does not require a climax, and that is in intercourse under the conditions prescribed in the Code of the Oneida Colony as a method of birth control. In accordance with their practise the man does not allow himself to have a climax and the usual duration of intercourse is from 1½ to 2½ hours, during which time the woman may experience several climaxes. Under these conditions of satiety the man no longer feels the need for an orgasm, and is perfectly satisfied and content at the end not to have one. Under this practice men feel the need for coitus no more often than do their wives; he is also more cognizant of the importance of coming to his wife at a time when she, too, feels the need, and in general the two are very happy with their sexual pattern and very successful in the matter of birth control.

It is very apparent that if a husband and wife are to provide each other with anything like a happy sex life they must recognize these differences in final response. This realization is especially important for the husband to acquire. He must appreciate that there are many times his wife will not reach a climax either because it was a night when her physical need for sexual release was not present, or because she was not adequately built up by an atmosphere of well-being, affection and love, or finally because his own climax was premature.

By understanding variations of this kind the couple can attain a much finer degree of sexual satisfaction.

4. *Anxiety over the matter of technique.* Many women brought up prudishly, and many men without the imagination to be adequate, artful lovers, conduct coitus with the routine monotony of the same procedure year after year, like animals. The whole affair naturally loses interest and grows stale for both of them.

To keep sexual interest in each other alive, and to give fullness and richness to requiting each other's needs, there is the same necessity here for creative expression and new experience that there is in any other aspect of life. Sexual experience between a hubsand and wife can be as creative and as beautiful as they are capable of making it, and it can be maintained through the years as the most precious part of their life together. Any procedure or innovation that increases the enjoyment and the beauty of the relationship for either one of them, without incurring the displeasure of the other, is entirely normal. They do not need to fear that this practise or that, one posture or another, this kind of a caress or that kind, is an indication of depravity or perversion. The sole criterion is that it pleases both. Their sex life is entirely and completely their private concern, and whatever brings mutual pleasure is good.

It is important that the wife's responses are active and not passive. He loves nothing so much as to have his best efforts returned with enthusiasm. He loves to be thrilled by the unexpected advances and participations of his wife. To be thrilled he needs only to catch sight of his wife in the nude, regardless of what kind of a figure she has. And to have her crawl into bed with him unexpectedly in the nude lifts him to Mt. Everest. The little innovation, the little new caress or response, mean a great deal to him, require so little, and do so much.

● **The Perspective of Sexual Compatibility and Marriage Success**

1. The influence of compatibility on marital success. We tend to overestimate the importance of sexual compatibility and happiness in the ultimate success of a marriage. Not that it isn't important, nor that it isn't the primary cause of the break up of many marriages. It can be and is. But it isn't *the* determining factor that many couples think it is; sexual compatibility or incompatibility is often a secondary matter. There are so many other factors that are important too in making marriage a success — factors such as being content with the arrangement of a husband's work and the wife's homemaking, seeing eye-to-eye on other interests, recreation, and activities, enjoying each other's companionship and society, being satisfied with the financial arrangement, taking pleasure in having and rearing a famliy.

Very frequently in a couple seeking divorce; their mutual

sexual happiness was the only satisfactory thing in the marriage. True, it probably became less satisfactory toward the end when, because of the general trouble and estrangement, the wife could no longer feel sexually agreeable either. In this couple's marriage it was the other factors listed above and in Chapter 11 that produced the rift.

The reverse situation is equally often true. A marriage can be fundamentally happy and successful for both husband and wife even when their sexual life has been satisfactory for neither. In such a case the two must have enough general maturity in other fields to be able to play down the sexual failure and capitalize on the good features.

A childless married couple I knew culminated an exceedingly and unusually happy married life with their 55th wedding anniversary. All their friends thought them singularly well matched and as compatible as any two people in the world's history. And they considered themselves so, too. Imagine the surprise of an examining physician when he learned, what no one else knew, that in their entire happy life together they had never experienced sexual intercourse. When the incapacity (the nature of which is irrelevant) became apparent to them early in their marriage, they experienced a short period of consternation. But their compatibility in other ways, their genuine affection and friendship for each other, and their general maturity, compensated for this sexual lack and they determined to overlook the difficulty and succeeded admirably, regardless of how much a psychiatrist would have discouraged them at that time.

2. *The time required to reach sexual compatibility in marriage.* It is also important to put into proper perspective the fact that approximately half of all newly married couples do not achieve good sexual adjustment until after a year of marriage, nearly 15 per cent require three years and 10 per cent become sexually well mated only after 20 years.[3]

A couple should therefore not despair if their sexual ex-

    [3] Judson T. Landis, "Length of Time Required to Achieve Adjustment in Marriage," *American Sociological Review*, 11: 666-77, December, 1946.

perience during the first year, or the first few years, has not been successful. It is very possible that they can still work it out. Something is wrong with the psychological outlook and attitude of one of them, or of both of them. A frank assessment and discussion between themselves or with an understanding physician or counselor will help. The trouble is almost never anatomical, that is to say, due to abnormality of the genital organs of either husband or wife.

● **The Perspective for Social Regulations and Tabus**

Many people feel the urge for extra-marital sexual experience, either before marriage or during marriage.

Some people would condemn such action on a purely moral basis, while many others in this 20th century no longer feel "moral" persuasion very strongly.

It is much more fruitful anyway to consider such deviation in the perspective of its basic effects. The type of action that is classed as "immoral" is the type of action which, if indulged in generally, would make our present society impossible, or it is the type of action that would harm one's personality structure. Opium smoking is a readily understood example.

There are some areas of society in the United States in which extra-marital sexual intercourse might almost be said to be fashionable and accepted by the miscreants as constituting the norm for that social group. This is not a good indication for the future well-being of American society.

1. The perspective of extra-marital sex activities in married people. When extra-marital sex relations occur in a marriage, it is first of all, and most importantly, an indication of failure on the part of both people to create, achieve, and maintain a good basic sexual union between them. Any man or woman given a completely unified, a creatively rich and satisfactory sexual experience by the spouse will feel revulsion at, rather than desire for, extra-marital affairs.

This is a law in marriage as specific as a law in physics. If your spouse wanders off, ask the question, "How have the two of us failed?" Then after trying your best to arrive at an understanding of your difficulties, take each other back and try again, more earnestly, more sincerely, more creatively, and most of all, more maturely.

Whenever a large number of extra-marital affairs are occurring in any portion of society, it indicates that there is something in the culture of these groups that is conditioning a general immaturity in more fields of living than in merely the sexual field. It is in these same groups that one finds a general low level of immaturity, one incapable of making marriage much of a success on any grounds. The fall of great empires, such as the Roman Empire, has been accompanied not only by sexual licentuousness, but by a cultural degeneration and immaturity in all other areas of living — in such matters as personal dishonesty, civic dishonesty, greed, selfishness, and in an emphasis on trivial pleasures rather than on good principle.

The same general pattern of immaturity exists in the individual as in his society. Society cannot long survive a general degeneration of the individual, nor can the alert individual stand idly by to allow a general lowering of the standards in society.

Marital unfaithfulness indicates first a sexual immaturity, and secondly, a general immaturity in most other fields.

Other undesirable features of marital unfaithfulness, such as failing in one's responsibility to one's children, or the personal trouble it needlessly injects into one's living, are essentially the same as those entailed in premarital sexual indulgence and can be included in the discussion of that subject.

2. *Sexual experience before marriage.* It is no easy matter for unmarried people to find a satisfactory sexual solution. There is none except a satisfactory marriage.

The findings of Dr. Alfred C. Kinsey are that 35 per cent of males admit premarital experience and he believes that because many tend to cover up this information, the true number is closer to 50 per cent. Women seem to be much less apt to have premarital affairs, and to be less interested in a variety of partners.

The bad features of premarital indulgence are very real; very real for society, and very real for the individual.

First, there is the very real danger of the greater likelihood of contracting venereal disease. Although venereal disease is relatively easily curable compared to 15 years ago, gonorrhea can still result in sterility in both the male and female before it is brought under control. And syphilis can still go undetected for years in the event an individual never has a Wassermann test.

Second, there is the very real danger of pregnancy, despite contraceptive measures. An illegitimate pregnancy means excrutiatingly poignant worries, apprehensions, and frustrations. Do not think for a minute it doesn't. It means also the choice between alternatives that are the worst of all misfortunes for the mother and baby – an illegitimate birth or an ill-advised marriage. There is evidence that illegitimate pregnancies force one out of every five marriages, and that divorce is many times higher in couples who marry because of an illegitimate conception.[4]

Thirdly, premarital experience has the psychological effect of cheapening the thing we call love. It lowers the value of the final marital experience in a very real way. It tends to emphasize the physical and to under-emphasize the total love picture that is so important to sexual success in marriage. The evidence shows that premarital promiscuity is a factor in producing frigidity in the female and marital maladjustment in both male and female.[5]

Fourthly, there are very real psychological injuries to the personality. Not only are there the personality-weakening factors of worry over venereal disease, missed periods, illegitimacy, forced marriage, abortion, and law proceedings, but there is the worry of the rightness and wrongness, fear of

---

[4] Harold T. Christensen, *Marriage Analysis*, New York: The Ronald Press Co., 1950, p. 153.

[5] *Ibid*, pp. 149 and 156. Also Margaret Banning, "The Case for Chastity," *Reader's Digest*, 31: 4-5, August, 1937.

being found out, fear of the future, fear of the true regard of one's partner, and one's offended sensitivities.[6]

Finally, there is the social stigma attached to all extra-marital sex practice. This stigma is a real consideration and cannot readily be overlooked and minimized. Nor can one take the attitude that what one does is one's own business and society had better change its mores. The reasons for social regulation and tabus in this field of sex are intrinsically sound and they cannot be thrown out without destroying human society. Society simply must tie responsibility to sexual opportunity in order to protect children, to reduce personal exploitation and justice, and to protect the women who have to bear and rear the children.

Developing a mature attitude toward sex that will eventually bring one an effective and happy sexual life depends fundamentally on placing all these factors, along with one's own sexual urges and outlook, into a correct perspective.

Only then is one prepared to form a mature attitude.

● The Mature Attitude on the Sexual Side of Life

The mature attitude that can turn the matter of sex from a constant aggravation and an irritating source of trouble into a worthy and adequate part of one's life, insists *first of all* on the recognition that success in its accomplishment will depend on something considerably better than clandestine and fragmentary encounters. It demands that sex becomes a frank and open part of the entire marriage relationship.

To be durable and satisfying, the pattern of one's sexual life must be created within the pattern of total companionship with one person of the other sex, to whom we can give our complete, undivided and fundamental love.

The word "love," unfortunately, is such an evasive, insecure term, that it connotes many different things to different people. So it is much clearer and safer to say that one's sexual life can attain its full meaning and fruition only with the one person for whom we feel the most sincere and the most genuine kind

---

[6] *Ibid*, p. 155.

of *friendship* we are capable of — "friendship" meaning devotion, honesty, openness, fairness, unselfishness, tenderness, understanding, loyalty, consideration and, above all, affection. True friendship is a hard thing to "service," and calls for a person who has a wide general maturity.

If you can bring these qualities to another person who has them too, you will see why we have used so many ultimate and superlative terms in the definition we have just given of the mature sexual attitude; sexual experience on these terms will constitute just about the finest and most precious part of your life.

Love is the combination of sex and deep friendship. The trouble with a lot of love is that it is mostly sex and very little friendship.

One more emphasis upon affection! Affection is the most important ingredient in friendship and it is the key to sex. Two people may have exciting physical experiences in sex, but there is no lasting satisfaction without affection. With affection two people get a warm feeling of contentment just by being in the same room together, or they find a beautiful happiness by lying in each other's arms without any further physical contact. When affection and the other qualities of friendship are added to the natural body functions of sex, the physical and psychological experience that emerges is the thing for which the human race has coined such terms as "beautiful," "supreme," "sublime," and "ultimate."

Affection must never be taken for granted in the everybody routine of married life. A woman, and a man too, needs to be told, "I love you." She (and he also) likes to receive a kiss or a hug in the kitchen or on the basement stairs as well as in bed, and she (and he) will prove to be a much more wonderful bed partner if there has been affection and true friendship during the day.

The mature attitude is the same attitude for men and for women. Both must feel that when they join sexually they are no longer two people with separate sensory rhythms, separate desires and feelings, but that they are, if they are mature, one person with two parts, each part having concern not for itself but for the other.

The child that is born, so like and so identical to both, is the final proof that two people *can* and need to become one.

● *Starting a Mature Sexual Perspective in the Children*

Sexual maturity is obviously a matter which can only be *initiated* in children and must wait until adult life for final development. But it must be started properly in childhood.

Without doubt, this is one of the most difficult duties of parenthood, and consequently one that is often very poorly handled.

Sometimes parents hope to dismiss their responsibility on the subject with a 15-minute session on "the facts of life" when their children's adolescence approaches. Some parents even side-step that.

It is presumptuous to think that such a session will accomplish much in a constructive way, because the chances are the youth already knows much more than you are going to tell him in 15 or 30 minutes.

How much do children know about sex? Conclusions based upon personal interviews with 291 pre-adolescent and adolescent boys from middle class and upper middle class families showed that:

> All had a considerable amount of sex information before they were ten. By age 14, nearly all had a fair idea of the process of human reproduction. Over 95 per cent by the age of 14 knew about the origin of babies, masturbation, intercourse, and prostitution. Over 86 per cent at 14 knew about contraception. Half at this age knew about venereal diseases. Ninety per cent of these boys had gotten their information from companions. Parents had little part in the giving of sex information.[7]

Girls in general have a comparable knowledge at the same age, but much more of their knowledge comes from their

---

[7] J. T. Landis, and M. G., *Building a Successful Marriage*, (Englewood Cliffs, N. J.: Prentice-Hall, Inc., 1953)

parents, particularly the mother, than it does in the case of boys.

When is the child old enough to be told facts about sex? When he is old enough to ask questions like "How do birds fly?", "Where do babies come from?", "Why is the sky blue?" The answer to any of these should be as accurate as possible and complete enough to answer the question. As Landis says, "When children first start asking questions, biologically complete answers are not needed any more than a complete explanation is needed of the functioning of the internal combustion engine the first time the child asks what makes the car go." When he is older and asks specific questions, he should be given specific answers.

Fortunately only 5 per cent of children ask the most difficult question of what part the father plays in getting the baby started. Most children probably know enough about the matter to feel as embarrassed in asking the question as parents feel in answering it. If the question is asked, it should be answered accurately that father and mother are different biologically and that the father is constructed so that his cells may unite with the mother's and start a baby.

Between the ages of eight and ten, menstruation should be explained to girls as a part of normal growing up. It should never be referred to as a sickness or a handicap but something which all women have and handle easily as a part of their lives.

Parents may buy some of the excellent books that have been written on the subject for children and place them casually where the children may pick them up, rather than assign them a special reading.

For grade school children:

M. I. Levine, J. H. Seligman, *The Wonder of Life, How We are Born and How We Grow Up.* New York: Simon and Schuster, Inc., 1940, 114 pp.

F. B. Strain, *Being Born, a Book of Facts for Boys and Girls.* Appleton-Century-Crofts, Inc., 1936, 144 pp.

For junior high school children:

A. Novikoff, *From Head to Foot.* New York: International Publishers, Inc., 1946, 96 pp.

F. B. Strain, *Teen Days*. New York: Appleton-Century-Crofts, Inc., 1946, 183 pp.
References for parents on sex education for children:
J. T. Landis, and M. G. Landis, *Building a Successful Marriage*. Englewood Cliffs, N. J.: Prentice-Hall, Inc., 1953, Chapter 23, Sex Education.
James L. Hyme, *How to Tell Your Children about Sex*. New York: Public Affairs Committee, 1949, pamphlet No. 149.
F. B. Strain, *New Patterns in Sex Teaching*. New York: Appleton-Century-Crofts, Inc., 1951, 262 pp.
F. B. Strain, *Sex Guidance in Family Life Education*. New York: The Macmillan Company, 1942, 340 pp.

Two things that it is wise to get over to teen-agers are these: First, that there are people with unhealthy and warped attitudes about sex, such as exhibitionists and homosexuals, and simply to avoid them if they ever meet with them. The second is that uncontrolled sex impulses will cause them as much harm and trouble as an uncontrolled automobile.

Parents usually meet some form of socially unacceptable childhood activity in sex. These should be dealt with by explanation that adult people don't do such things, and children do not either, rather than that they are bad and shocking in themselves. Children undressing each other at play is done usually to find out how the other is made and whether anyone is the same. Assurance that all boys are alike and all girls are alike will usually stop further investigation. Children sometimes indulge in sex experimentation. It should be made clear that sexual union is for married people only and that if sexual union occurs before that, it may have a disastrous effect on their whole lives.

There is no need for a parent to deal with the child's sexual problems or questions fiercely or angrily. A kindly approach in which explanations are as complete as the child's understanding warrants, and in which the reasons for sexual restraint are explicitly given, will do much more good for the child's proper adjustment.

13

Having an Interest Beyond
One's Own Little World

A child has no interests beyond itself and the small circle that its eyes encompass.

But a mature person has a genuine and deep interest in people and in the great wide world with its magnificent variety of fascinating subjects.

Such an interest in things and people will add greatly to any woman's personal enjoyment in life. It will also help her immeasurably in dealing with other people, especially in enriching the lives of the members of her immediate family.

● Women Are More Naturally Interested in People Than in Things

An interest in other *people* comes more naturally to a woman than to a man because of the human sympathies in the role of motherhood.

But many women are woefully lacking in an interest in other *things*—"things" being a term to include the subject matter of the great wide world. This type of interest in things is acquired more readily by men than by women, because of their role in business and political affairs and in the workaday world.

As this maturity grows, interests increase in intensity and

211

in scope. To the mature person everything is interesting, everything invites participation. Naturally, because of the time factor, active interests must be narrowed down to one or two fields.

But in spite of this narrowing, the capacity for wide interest is there, and the mature person can leave off reading history, and take up poetry, or leave ornithology and take up butterfly collecting at anytime.

This maturity, then, is really an interest-capacity.

It is more than just having a hobby, although a hobby may very well be a part of it.

It is an interest in what is going on in one's world, and participating in it, as much as one's time will allow, in a knowledgeable and perhaps in an active way.

It is an interest in the world of both nature and people, and even though one cannot find the time to pursue anything very extensively, yet the interest-capacity for it is there.

The difference between Mary and Sally. Sally and Mary were in the same class in high school, both "A" students, and both beautiful girls. There was one glaring difference between the two girls, however.

Sally had no interests. She took the school courses because they were prescribed, but no great interest in any of them was ever awakened, although she did very well in her school work in a memorizing sort of way. She had no great interest in any activity, no interest in athletics, and only a slight interest in dancing. Boys and other girls did not find her much fun, and seldom asked her to go out.

Mary, on the other hand, was interested in just about *everything*. She *lived* American history and her other courses; something new immediately found her aglow; she burst into life over physics. She belonged to the Camera Club, the Dramatics Club, the *Philatelics* Club, the Dance Club, and loved them all. She liked athletics. Mary was popular with everyone because she could find mutual interests with everyone, and everyone found her interesting. Every boy in her class wanted to date her.

Sally had as high an I.Q. as Mary did, and it was Sally who

had the better grades. Sally ended up valedictorian and Mary salutatorian. Mary might have surpassed Sally had she wanted to and had she had enough time from all her activities.

The difference between the two girls was that in Sally the spark of interest had never kindled a fire, or her battery of interest-capacity had never been charged; it was dead. Sally's parents had no interests. Her family life was a routine of the usual trivialities; the family conversation was on minor routine matters; the interest-capacity battery of her whole family was dead.

But Mary's interest capacity had been awakened by a mother and a father who themselves had wide, keen interests and had the knack of passing it on to their children.

● **The General Importance of Interest-Capacity to a Woman**

One important reason why she needs the perspective of wide interests is because a woman must rear a family of children that can meet the world on an understanding basis. She starts gaining this perspective in the education she receives, but she must carry it on herself from there.[1]

But equally important, the modern woman needs the maturity of interest-capacity to enrich her own life in the years before and after the family grows up.

She needs it, too, in making a better, more meaningful life with her husband. With a mature capacity she will be able to adopt the interests he has, as well as to contribute new ones to their life together.

● **The Importance of Common Interests in Living with a Husband**

There is no question but that a wife and husband will have a more satisfactory life together if they have one or more durable interests in common.

This is not to say that two people cannot live agreeably and be mutually happy even if each pursues entirely different interests. But the chances of success favor the couple with the

---

[1] Woman's formal education in the United States is better than man's education. She receives an average of 10.7 years, he an average of 9.9 years. (*Life*, December 24, 1956, Vol. 41, No. 26, page 2.)

ability to interest themselves in the same projects. Certainly such a cooperative and mutually interested pair can provide their children with a richer family life simply by bringing their children into the same mutual project.

1. The marriage of two people who have no interests. Any person who has never developed an interest-capacity leads a dull, colorless, bored life. And when a man and a woman, both without an interest, marry, their life together will be twice as dull as if they had lived alone.

Their lives together have no direction. Their leisure time is entirely lacking in value and becomes a source of petty irritations and gross trouble. There are a tremendous number of rudderless couples like this in the United States.

Such a couple try to fill their time with small parties and catch-as-catch-can activities like a show or a night club, the sort of thing that becomes deadly dull and uninspiring in a short time. The most readily available aid for tossing off their boredom is an increasing amount of bourbon. Drinking among couples has increased tremendously in the past 20 years. About the only interest that is available to their weak imagination is an extra-marital sexual affair. These have become alarmingly common in our American society, especially in this group who lack interest-capacity and have no keen interests.

The leisure-principle of our day poses a real problem. Urban people, especially the husband, or the wife without children, have *much more* leisure today than people did before 1920. Finding adequate ways for filling this leisure has actually become one of the critical problems in modern marriage.

Unless this leisure time can be filled satisfactorily—satisfactorily for both of them, and with interests that are enduring and rewarding—it becomes an irritating and troublesome spot that has helped ruin many a marriage.

A woman actively engaged in rearing children has little leisure, but her husband still has his, and if he has no worthy interests with which to occupy himself he can drift into the trivial activities that lead to extra-marital trouble more quickly because his wife is not with him.

Her husband's leisure always remains a woman's concern. She will do well to pick a man who has solid, durable interests, even though they may not be her own. She should try, of course, to make them her own.

It is a grave error to think that a person who has no interests before marriage will develop interests after marriage. He may do so, of course, if the spouse is a good teacher with the capacity to stimulate interest. But the chances are against it. In his youth the development of an interest-capacity maturity was given no start.

This error is so apt to be made when two people suddenly and romantically fall in love and decide, after the second or third meeting, that further life is impossible without immediate marriage.

Joan and Carl met at a friend's cocktail party, fell romantically in love at once, and married two weeks later. Each had been married before; each had been divorced after two years, in both cases largely because they had nothing in common with the spouse except sex. When they met, they misinterpreted mutual sexual needs as constituting a deeply kindred spirit, and without waiting to find out very much more about the other, they married.

Joan had interests she could have developed with a little encouragement and assistance. She liked to read, had a genuine love for poetry and literature, an excellent appreciation of music, was a good pianist, had a real love for nature, and a tremendous ability to entertain and be a hostess. But Carl had not a single extra-sexual interest, not even work, except a desire to be an opera singer. His voice, however, was too temperamental even for barroom use.

Joan was discouraged within a week after marriage. Carl did not want to read, did not like to drive out into the woods for a Sunday outing, did not want to talk about anything. He desired only to spend his free time at night clubs and in taverns carrying on trivial conversations with half-inebriated friends to the accompaniment of loud phonograph music.

Joan sincerely tried to meet him on the grounds of his own

interest, and made the rounds with him. But the interest was not only inadequate but served as a road to new trouble. Carl had been frequently drunk before marriage. He became more and more frequently drunk after marriage. He was naturally pouty and sarcastic, and became increasingly so as the romantic polish wore off their marriage.

Joan's final reaction to Carl's general drunkenness and disagreeableness was a sexual distaste and withdrawal.

The marriage did not last long after that.

It is this type of blindness to the other requirements of a good marriage that is the worst thing about romantic love, which is in large part a sexual urge.

Nor should a woman expect a husband to develop her interests after marriage. Most men are immature in their flexibility and adaptability and have a poorly developed degree of enlightened selfishness. It is most often the wife who relinquishes her interests and takes up those of the husband.

Many a girl has relinquished her entire set of relative values, her philosophy of life, her ideals of one kind and another and adopted her husband's in order to achieve some unity of purpose and outlook. A girl will give up her lifelong desire for a modern-type house and modernistic furniture and go along with her husband's ideal of a colonial house and furniture. She may have been a militant member of one political party while in college but readily takes up her husband's when she marries. It is seldom that the man makes similar concessions of adaptation.

So often during courtship the girl counts on the fact that the boy is so devotedly in love with her that he will gladly mold himself into the image she has created for him and change in the ways she has set for him. This idea is a part of the unrealism and idealization that is known as *romantic love*, so commonly the basis for marriage in the United States.

2. *The marriage of two people with different interests.* The marriage of two people with different interests is less likely to end in trouble than the marriage of two people with no interests. At least they each have something to take up their spare time and to occupy their minds.

Some couples develop several common interests in the time before the children come. Then for 20 or 25 years the wife is largely occupied with rearing the family, and the husband goes ahead following the interests they have started or develops some new ones of his own. When she is again freed from the care of children she often turns to interests of her own, leaving the husband to his, and they are perfectly happy and content.

If each of them have separate and distinct interests, they can get along very well, if each will simply tolerate and recognize the legitimacy of the other's activities. Before they marry it is advisable that neither of them should expect that the other will take up his particular interests. Such expectation will usually lead to trouble and to disappointment.

Agnes and Jack were romantically in love. Their marriage was to be utter happiness. It could not fail because their love was so delightfully, so uniquely, so completely ideal that a blissful marriage was foreordained and meant to be.

Agnes liked dancing, music, bridge, and reading. Jack liked boating, hunting, and fishing. Agnes counted on the fact that Jack's loving devotion would change his interests to hers after they were married. She couldn't possibly see how she could take up Jack's. She was afraid of insects, snakes, water, and poison ivy, and abhorred mosquitoes; she disliked roughing it and cooking outside.

Jack, for his part, hated music, reading, dancing, and bridge, and he thought Agnes could get over her silly ideas and adopt his interests.

For years Agnes tried to change Jack, and Jack tried to change Agnes. They had many an unnecessary spat and much unhappiness and trouble. It could very easily have broken up their marriage if the both hadn't been fairly mature in other respects.

Now each goes his own way. Jack hunts and fishes, Agnes reads and plays bridge. They are happy enough and content to let the other do as he pleases.

The children in such a family lack the benefits of all-family projects, and they tend, like father and mother, to develop interests of their own.

The trouble with Agnes and Jack was that they both had stopped at the half-way mark in their maturity of interest-capacity. Had either of them a well-rounded interest-capacity they would have no trouble meeting on the common ground of the same interests.

Mary and Bill wove a different pattern together than did Agnes and Jack.

Mary, whom we described earlier in this chapter, grew up in a family that was much more mature in its interests than Agnes' family. Mary had a mature interest-capacity, a wide range of interests, and a quick appreciation of new interests. She liked practically any kind of activity.

When Mary married Bill (who like so many men had Jack's love for hunting and fishing), she easily developed a genuine liking for that sort of thing and went with Bill whenever she could. She got Bill interested in addition, in two closely allied hobbies—photography and ornithology. Bill later added some more that Mary accepted — archery, arrow-making, and hunting for Indian arrowheads. As the children came they all took part in mother's and father's activities, and they all made a very smooth-functioning, happy family.

The woman who comes to marriage with a mature interest-capacity will be capable of leading a richer and happier life with her husband than the woman who does not.

● *The Aid of a Mature Interest-Capacity in Rearing Children*

The wider the range of a woman's interests, and the more mature her interest-capacity, the more interesting her children will be and the smoother her family will run. This assumes that she is fairly mature in other respects, as she probably will be, for a mature interest-capacity usually means that she will be interested also in the maturities.

We have higher standards today in raising children than we did 50 years ago, and a better chance of good results, just as this is equally true in medicine, dentistry, electrical work, plumbing, and most other lines of work.

But improved products call for more skill and better knowledge. Some of these skills the woman has acquired in her formal education, but most of them she will have to dig up for herself, and can dig up for herself if she has a mature interest-capacity.

Although mother's time is limited, there is enough time somewhere to be able to crowd in some reading or even a short course or two on such matters as infant feeding, nourishing the child, understanding the child and helping him grow up, helping him realize his possibilities. Not every woman can be an expert on all the phases of a child's development, but every woman can be an expert at being interested in the subject.

But even more important to the mother is the way in which a rich field of interests on her part can help her children attain a mature attitude by the time they are ready to fit into the modern world. Even if she doesn't have time to read much on her own, reading to the children ten minutes a day or every other day, will direct them into the wonderful realms of Christopher Robin, Winnie the Poo, Rutabaga Land, and the Wind in the Willows.

Though she may have little time for reading the papers and the weekly commentary, her interest and curiosity can stimulate the high school youngster to a similar interest.

Knowing a little about everything herself, she can introduce and encourage the children in various activities, in painting, leatherwork, woodwork, knitting, sewing, and all manners of projects.

She will be able to transmit as much to the children as her own range of interest and interest-capacity allows her.

● The Value of a Mature Interest-Capacity in Her Own Life

All of us, including mother herself, tend to forget that she is an individual in her own right, even though she spends all her time giving herself away to other people. She, too, deserves a life she can call her own.

We forget that mother has basic psychological needs too. Like everyone else she needs not only affection and security, but to be happy she needs creative expression and to have new experiences like anyone else.

During the child-rearing years these needs are well provided for in the very services she gives the children. But it is during the time before the children come, and in the longer years after the children are gone, or in a childless marriage, that the woman needs interests and interest-capacity as much as a sailboat needs a keel to keep it upright and on a straight course.

So much of what is wrong with women after the children have left home comes from the fact that they are utterly devoid of interests, like the man who retires with nothing to occupy his mind. During the years they gave everything to the family, the husbands have grown into their own fields of interest, and she is alone. Her few social activities, a bridge club, a reading club, are not enough to put wind in her sails.

The need of interests becomes greater as time passes on, for there is not only the possibility, but the probability (since women usually outlive men) that her husband will die before her. Then the emptiness of life really needs to be filled.

Here is where Mary's type, with her wide interests and a mature interest-capacity formed in girlhood, will be able to handle the situation. She will always retain the capacity to enter new fields and start new interests. The Grandma Moses who starts painting in her late years is a woman who has always possessed great and deep interests in things.

14 ✒︎

Being Self=Reliant

Maturity No. 11

The foremost desire of parents who make a home and raise children is that their children grow up to be worthy, dependable adults. Most parents are willing to sacrifice more effort, time, and money to help their children than for any other purpose.

Consequently it is so sad when the children grow up to become *physically* mature but remain too *psychologically* immature to be ever capable of anything even approaching a happy life. So very often parents' good intentions produce such unintended and woefully immature children.

Really the parents should not be blamed. The blame should be placed somewhere in our total educational program. The parents are not to blame that no one has given them a better vision and more adequate knowledge for doing the job right.

● Failure of the Home to Teach Self-Reliance

The saddest failure any home can have is to be unable to give the child the most essential quality an adult must eventually possess—self-reliance—the ability to handle his own affairs.

All maturing is, in a sense, a growing away from the parents, the gradual liberation from the parasitic dependence of the fetus, and the suckling dependence of the infant, to the status of an independent adult capable of deciding his own living. Animals push their young out into the world at an early age. But human beings are children for a long time; so long sometimes they may never entirely get over it, especially if they are not taught certain adult ways. One of the most essential things about an adult is that he be able to sail his own craft without continued dependence on parental help.

All through life every human being is the epicenter of opposing motives or drives. No two opposite drives are harder to resolve than the childish drive toward the continued help and security of the parents on the one hand, and the drive for an independence and freedom of his own on the other. The conflict is especially strong in adolescence, and is one of the factors that makes that period so turbulent.

Too many parents enjoy this clinging to childhood, and deliberately try to keep their children always children.

Other parents are overanxious about their children; they try too hard to protect them and help them, even after they are working and married. All through the child's life these too well-meaning parents make all the decisions for the child, even on minor matters which the child could very well be left to decide for himself, if only as a matter of practice and development. And what is even worse, these parents are constantly reversing and revising whatever decision the child does make. He is made to think he is incapable of ever making his own decisions.[1]

The result is just what one would expect—an arrest in a childhood state of dependence. They are never able to make a go of adult life; they feel unable to make decisions. They do not recognize problems in their true light, they cannot solve problems. They need to run to someone for help. This someone will be mother or father while they are still alive.

---

[1] Theoretically there is one other way in addition to those given above in which a person may suffer an arrest in childhood dependence. That is by forcing children prematurely into work and responsibility, so that the child "freezes" into a longing for dependence, help and security other than its own efforts. Such cases are very rare today in modern American life where children are very rarely put out on their own so soon.

And when they die their adult child will feel more insecure than ever.

A wife runs to her mother with every problem she meets in marriage from baking a pie to her husband's halitosis. The husband resents this intrusion of outside opinion into his home, and in-law trouble begins. He resents the implications of the mother-in-law's interference as he would the old saying, "It takes two good women to make a good husband."

When the mother is no longer available, either because she dies or one of the families move away, the wife becomes utterly unable to make decisions of even a moderate sort. She begins to take hours doing small jobs, even forgetting very often what she had started out to do. She is unable to stand up to any situation without crying. The usual result is that she ruins her marriage, her husband's life, and her children's future.

When these people are very immature, they drift to the fringe of humanity where they are easy suckers for demagogues and exploiters of every low variety. They quite readily become criminals of low order, prostitutes, perverts, or some other variety of irregular.

Other individuals with a slightly greater degree of self-reliance may get along fairly well when they have all sorts of support from friends, relatives and others. They are the ones who through high school are always needing to study with someone else, especially at examination time. They need always to be asking everyone for help on their home problems, the minister for help in family matters, the doctor for constant help in anticipated illnesses. Because the ready source of dependence and security they had in childhood is gone, they are continually anxious and tense with their helplessness in the face of the stream of problems that comprise daily living. In a desperate attempt to compensate for their deficiency and inadequacy, they throw themselves into situations aggressively and unpleasantly, a combination of emotions that can lead to peptic ulcers.[2]

---

[2] John A. Schindler, *How to LIVE 365 Days a Year* (Englewood Cliffs, N.J.: Prentice-Hall, Inc., 1955), pp. 48-49.

Another form of attempted compensation occurs in boys with undeveloped independence. They try to demonstrate to their fellows and to themselves how mature they are and take up early cigarette smoking, drive the car like a racer, engage in delinquencies, and even gangsterism.

Higher up on the scale of maturity are the individuals who can operate with reasonable independence until some hardship, or some unusual situation, throws them back on their childhood necessity for dependence and help. These people quickly seek solace and comfort in alcohol or barbiturates. They also demonstrate another interesting psychological phenomenon in that they may "regress"—that is, go back to a completely childish attitude of dependence, losing all the independence they once had. This is more apt to occur if the offending hardship or difficulty is of extended duration. This, of course, is the sort of thing loosely termed a neurosis, which is a very early childhood arrest in any line of development.

Psychologically, a regression is a reconditioning of a deconditioned reflex. In childhood, the feelings of insecurity and anxiety that are a reflex part of having to meet a problem without help, are gradually deconditioned as one attains a certain amount of confidence. But later on in life a problem which initially is a very difficult one, strongly brings back the childhood feelings of insecurity and anxiety. As the same difficult problem continues, the feelings of insecurity and anxiety begin to occur again in decisions of lesser and lesser magnitude, until the childhood state has again been established. This is simply recalling or reconditioning an old reflex mechanism which had once been very strong and is easily recovered.

● *How to Develop Self-Reliance in Later Life*

Learning self-reliance in adult life, after it has been absent since childhood, or after it has been lost by a regression, is hard and takes time. Prevention is easier by far.

Is there much help for the adult who is ruining her life, and her family's, because of a continued dependence on others for help?

Assuredly there is. There is much that can be done for her. There is much she can do for herself.

First of all, the person who finds it hard to make decisions and meet responsibility must realize precisely what the trouble is. She must realize that she has never matured beyond a childhood dependence on someone for her decisions. The degree of self-reliance she did acquire is not sufficient for the role in which adulthood has cast her. As the problems of her adult world become steadily more complex and more numerous, her small measure of self-reliance shrinks to miserably inadequate proportions.

Why cannot she make a decision, just as you and I? Because her preadult training did not give her the confidence that she could do it. She feels *incapable* of solving important problems. When an important problem comes up, she is seized with the conditioned emotion of anxiety, insecurity, fear, and frustration. She wants to run to someone for help, or just run. Friction and difficulties with the husband and in the home give her the same feeling she would have had if at age four she had become separated from mother and father in a great crowd, had found herself surrounded by utter strangers.

She must look back into her childhood and see how her mother protected her from meeting problems and making decisions; how, whenever she did take the initiative, someone was forever altering her decision and deciding it had better be done some other way.

This basic understanding of her difficulty she may be able to uncover for herself, if she can muster up enough objectivity. This is hard for her simply because, as we have said, these people recognize and analyze existing problems poorly. It may be necessary for some observing friend or a doctor to help them get this initial bird's-eye view of themselves.

The second step is to realize just exactly what it is they feel when they are faced with a decision. They need to know and realize that this awful feeling is the physical manifestation of the mixed emotion of anxiety, fear, frustration—the tightening in the chest and in breathing, an inward tremor in the body, lightheadedness, an abdominal "sinking," and so on. These things *are* the emotion that comes on automatically as a conditioned reflex when a decision is being called for. It is expressed by the formula:

(a decision to make) + (no mother around to make it) = (feeling of anxiety and frustration)

It is the same sort of thing as the fear that comes with even a minor storm in someone who has had a severe experience with lightning.

This reflex emotion of anxiety will not disappear readily. It will keep coming on to some degree even after the person begins to make decisions.

She must realize what this feeling is, and why it comes. When it comes she must talk to herself just as she would to an anxious child who had lost her mother, gently, sympathetically, reassuringly, *and with an air of confidence* that no harm is going to result.

The third step is, despite this reflex emotion of anxiety, deliberately to make a decision, and to keep practising making decisions. One's intelligence is not at its best when one has a strong anxiety emotion, and one's evaluation of a problem may not be accurate, and one's decision not too good. But make the decision anyway! For no other reason than to begin getting the habit of making decisions.

Make the decision one way or the other. If your husband understands the problem, he will help by not accusing you of being foolish because of some of your decisions. Some of the first ones may be foolish. But we all make foolish decisions; even your husband does. Make the decision! What if it is wrong! All of us are wrong plenty of times anyway. So what? We should regard our own and other's mistakes tolerantly.

Then go ahead! On the first day start by coming to a snap decision on at least *one* matter. The second day take a flying leap and jump the hurdle of indecision on at least *two* matters. Each day add one more decision until you reach five a day. Then keep practicing five, day after day. Another help is an educational device used in childhood. Engage in activities in which solving problems proceeds according to methods and rules. Play checkers, chess, bridge, cribbage, euchre. Work crossword puzzles, or cut-out puzzles, go to vocational or adult education school and take a course in anything that even slightly interests you.

All of the time, keep assuring yourself, with an assumed air of confidence, that you can mature in this as well as anyone else, even though it may be a bit later and a bit harder for being late. Assure and tell yourself it can be done, and that you are going to do it!

Plain dogged determination, stupid determination if you wish, to overcome difficulties is a powerful and great human capacity that is not resorted to often enough in psychotherapy.

Finally, another excellent aid is to join up with a Dale Carnegie Club in your area. There probably is one nearby.

Dale Carnegie Clubs, through both expertly directed and mutual aids, help the individual walk up to problems with confidence and assurance, to counter problems by positive action. I have advised many people who lacked confidence and decisiveness to join them, with almost uniformly excellent results.

● *Parent Responsibility in the Parent-Child Relationship*

In your own children you will wish to develop the confidence, self-reliance and mature independence that is so vitally necessary in adult living.

Self-reliance is taught to a very considerable extent in school, but it is made, broken, or arrested at home.

Children, just as soon as they are able, should be given tasks to perform commensurate with their age, and further performances should be encouraged by the reward of praise and approval. These may be tasks like finding a box big enough to hold their toys, and picking a paint color for it to go with the walls. As they get older tasks should involve as much responsibility as is safe for the child.

The children should also be initiated into interesting problem-solving games like puzzles, games such as checkers, dominoes, "Clue," "Monopoly," "Go to the Head of the Class," Charades, "Two for the Money," crossword puzzles, and many others.

Encourage them to reach decisions that affect them, such as how they want their room furniture arranged, which of two lamps to buy for their room, whether to wear one dress or another, whether to walk downtown along 5th Street or along 6th Street. Avoid constantly choosing and deciding for them. With increasing age allow them more important decisions and more important responsibilities. Any questionable decision is opportunity for discussing and illustrating the trick of considering all the factors involved. A decision by a young driver to drive a car of teenagers to a night game 50 miles away shouldn't be jumped on tyranically, but a reconsideration presented in an objective, reasonable way. If the tenor of family relationship has been a reasonable one, the chances are you will convince him without too much trouble to discard the plan. But if you need finally to countermand the plan, do it reasonably by explaining it is your prerogative to be an unpopular parent sometime in the interest of what appears to you to be best for all.

If the child starts something on his own initiative, encourage it unless it involves something destructive like tearing a part of the house down.

The family is a place where a child can begin to exercise his right to be and act as an individual, where he can train himself in making correct decisions, where he can become expert in handling people and meeting responsibility. He can practice only as the parents allow him to practice.

It will often be hard for parents to decide how far to let the child go in his own decisions. On the whole, personal danger and other's rights being eliminated from consideration, it is generally better to give a child too much, than too little, leeway. Self-reliance is so important as to be worth a few mistakes in developing it.

15

How to Develop Your

Own Maturity

The attitudes stated in this book are the irreducible minimum of the maturities a well-rounded adult needs in order to handle the majority of adult situations in a way that is beneficial to himself and to everyone else involved in each situation.

Some people may, of course, wish to cross some off, or add others. That is certainly their prerogative. We felt that our list is a fairly universally acceptable one.

At various stages of the Wyalusing Conferences some of us wished to include as specific maturities some of the qualities which Benjamin Franklin called *Temperance, Order, Frugality, Justice, Moderation, Cleanliness,* and *Humility.* But we finally agreed that the important connotations of these terms were already included in the attitudes we had selected.

At another time some of us wanted to make separate maturities of *a feeling of responsibility,* and *seeing things through;* but finally we concluded that these were really a part of *liking to work.*

It was also suggested, for instance, that *an ability to withstand frustration* should be given the dignity of being a separate maturity. But on further consideration it was decided that this was contained in *making the most of it.*

229

● *A System for Developing the Maturities*

The order in which the maturities have been presented was made with an eye to a system any person may use for acquiring them.

Thus *a pleasant disposition* is listed first because it is one of the easiest to supervise in oneself, and one of the most delightful to try on for a fitting.

Once you are well on your way toward a pleasant disposition the other maturities are easier to attain. Having a pleasant disposition and a sense of humor will facilitate acquiring the second, *making the most of it*. And once you have started with the knack of making the most of it, you are ready to tackle the most difficult and the most essential, *being unselfish and having consideration for others*.

With these three well started the next eight maturities fall into place one after the other.

The system was developed successfully in medical practise. In his medical practise, the male member of the Wyalusing Conference has, over a period of 15 years, developed a successful method by which his patients with emotionally induced illness can go about acquiring the maturity which they lack, and whose lack has produced the emotional stress responsible for their illness.

The nice thing about this method is that it works. It has been used by thousands of patients with emotionally induced illness who badly needed their maturities overhauled. It can be used by anyone—anyone who desires to become more mature.

Benjamin Franklin originated the system. The method herein presented was originated, at least in its essential features, by Benjamin Franklin 200 years ago to develop what he at that time termed the "virtues," but which are practically the same thing we now call "maturities."

It was about 1730, when Franklin was 24 years old and was becoming established in Philadelphia, that he conceived his plan.

> It was about this time I conceived the bold and arduous project of arriving at moral perfection. I

wished to live without committing any fault at any time; I would conquer all that either natural inclination, custom, or company might lead me into. As I knew, or thought I knew, what was right and wrong, I did not see why I might not always do the one and avoid the other. But I soon found I had undertaken a task of more difficulty than I had imagined. While my care was employed in guarding against one fault, I was often surprised by another; habit took the advantage of inattention; inclination was sometimes too strong for reason. I concluded, at length, that the mere speculative conviction that it was our interest to be completely virtuous was not sufficient to prevent our slipping; and that the contrary habits must be broken and good ones acquired and established before we can have any dependence on a steady, uniform rectitude of conduct. For this purpose I therefore contrived the following method.

He made a list of all the moral virtues he had met in his reading.

I proposed to myself for the sake of clearness to use rather more names with fewer ideas annexed to each than a few names with more ideas; and I concluded under thirteen names of virtues all that at that time occurred to me as necessary or desirable and annexed to each a short precept which fully expressed the extent I gave to its meaning.

These names of virtues with their precepts were:

1. Temperance

Eat not to dullness; drink not to elevation.

2. Silence

Speak not but what may benefit others or yourself; avoid trifling conversation.

3. Order

Let all your things have their places; let each part of your business have its time.

4. Resolution

Resolve to perform what you ought; perform without fail what you resolve.

5. Frugality

Make no expense but to do good to others or yourself; i.e., waste nothing.

6. Industry

Lose no time; be always employed in something useful; cut off all unnecessary actions.

7. Sincerity

Use no hurtful deceit; think innocently and justly, and, if you speak, speak accordingly.

8. Justice

Wrong none by doing injuries or omitting the benefits that are your duty.

9. Moderation

Avoid extremes; forbear resenting injuries so much as you think they deserve.

10. Cleanliness

Tolerate no uncleanliness in body, clothes, or habitation.

11. Tranquility

Be not disturbed at trifles, or at accidents common or unavoidable.

12. Chastity

Rarely use venery but for health or offspring, never to dullness, weakness, or the injury of your own or another's peace or reputation.

Franklin next went about acquiring these precepts very methodically.

My intention being to acquire the habitude of all these virtues, I judged it would be well not to distract my attention by attempting the whole at once, but to fix it on one of them at a time; and, when I should be master of that, then to proceed to another, and so on, till I should have gone through the thirteen; and, as the previous acquisition of some might facilitate the acquisition of certain others, I arranged them with that view as they stand above.

I made a little book in which I allotted a page for each of the virtues, I ruled each page with red ink so as to have seven columns, one for each day of the week, marking each column with a letter for the day. I crossed these columns with thirteen red lines, marking the beginning of each line with the first letter of one of the virtues on which line and in its proper column I might mark by a little black spot, every fault I found upon examination to have committed respecting that virtue upon that day.

	S.	M.	T.	W.	T.	F.	S.
T.							
S.	*	*		*		*	
O.	**	*	*		*	*	*
R.			*			*	
F.		*			*		
I.			*				
S.							
J.							
M.							
C.							
T.							
C.							
H.							

Once Franklin had instituted this system he persisted in it all his life.

I entered upon the execution of this plan for self-examination and continued it with occasional intermissions for some time. I was surprised to find myself so much fuller of faults than I had imagined; but I had the satisfaction of seeing them diminish.

After a while I went through one course only in a year, and afterward only one in several years, till at length I omitted them entirely, being employed in voyages and business abroad with a multiplicity of affairs that interfered; but I always carried my little book with me.

● *How to Use the System to Develop Your Maturities*

The method used in the physician's office, modeled after Benjamin Franklin's, is as effective as it is simple.

Table No. 5, at the end of this chapter, is a chart prepared for your use.

The maturities are listed in the left-hand column, and the corresponding immaturities are listed in the opposite right-hand column. Between them are columns that will enable you to keep your record as Franklin did.

Write your starting date at the top of the first column.

Begin with the first maturity, *a predictably pleasant disposition.*

For three successive days watch yourself, paying special attention to your disposition, striving to keep it pleasant at all times. If you are reasonably successful in keeping your disposition spotless, leave the three spaces blank for each of the three days. But if your disposition gets out of hand and becomes nasty even for a little while make an X, or a check V, in the square for that day.

Having given the first maturity three days of special attention and emphasis, then go on to the second, *making the most of it,* and concentrate on it, trying to improve yourself in that, for the next three days, still paying attention, of course, to No. 1 already started, and continuing to mark down indiscretions you may commit in that.

Every three days you take on a new maturity for practise, continuing to practise those already added. Keep your score at the end of each day, very honestly and very candidly. Give more attention as time goes on to the maturity that continues to have the most X marks after it.

After the first run through and once you have been introduced to all the maturities, keep on tabulating your progress in the same way for the next two or three months.

Then after about six months check yourself again in all the maturities for a week to see how you are doing and to determine precisely where you still need to mature.

Being human like Franklin, or even a bit more human, you may awaken to the fact that you have forgotten to keep track for the past few days, one of those occasional intermissions Franklin speaks of. But go back to it again.

Or you may find that being a housewife keeps you too busy to follow the discipline very regularly just as did Franklin's, "being employed in voyages and business abroad with a multiplicity of affairs that interfered."

Even so, "carry (your) little book with you" and periodically check the columns as often as you can. Even by this halting procedure you will gain some benefit.

Worthy goals are, of course, the ones hardest to achieve, never easily nor without effort.

Perhaps you may be able to devise some other plan that will work out better for you than the one suggested here. But this one has been tried and proven.

Always, always keep this in mind:

The important thing for anyone, but especially for a woman, because her job and her career require a higher degree of it, is to grow up and become psychologically mature.

Table 5: A DAILY RECORD OF Y

Maturities	Page	Dates:											
1. A predictably pleasant disposition.	25												
2. Making the most of it.	50												
3. Enlightened selfishness; honest; considerate.	84												
4. Courageous; valiant.	108												
5. Not irritable nor angry.	122												
6. A tenderness for things human.	134												
7. Liking work.	142												
8. Mixing common sense with fancy.	160												
9. Making sex a happy part of living.	190												
10. Having interests beyond oneself.	211												
11. Self-reliance.	221												

GRESS IN DEVELOPING THE MATURITIES

																Immaturities
																1. Moody; sour; crabby; dull.
																2. Feeling abused; full of self-pity.
																3. Selfish, egotistical, dishonest.
																4. Fearful of vague dangers.
																5. Irritated and angered by tremendous trifles.
																6. Cruel, mean, hostile.
																7. Lazy, irresponsible.
																8. Accepting fancy as fact.
																9. Making a mess of sex.
																10. No interests beyond oneself.
																11. Indecisive, dependent on others.

The Wyalusing Setting

It was usually about nine o'clock on the fifth morning that the white webbing of the Bridgeport bridge towered over the two canoes as they passed beneath, paddles flashing in a rhythmic dip, dip, dip, sweeping down the final three-mile straightaway with Wyalusing looming grandly down stream and the Iowa bluffs of the Mississippi visible beyond.

Where the river meets the base of Wyalusing the two canoes turned out of the current into the lee of a natural stone jetty, where they were tied to trees at the water's edge. Each one of the five picked up a share of the camping gear, and in single file they toiled up the steep path through the woods to the crest of Wyalusing 600 feet above the river, groaning in mock agony as they climbed, the autumn woods sparkling more than ever with the girls' merriment.

As they crested the summit there were shouts of joy at the superb expanse of scenery spread out around them. With groans of relief they dropped their loads on a likely looking camp site on the very edge of the bluff overlooking the river, and set about making camp.

After a noon luncheon of mother's famous Wyalusing stew, the five set off down a wooded road to hold an afternoon conference in one of the many lovely spots with which Wyalusing abounds. Sometimes they hiked to Sentinel Ridge, the name given to the side of the Wyalusing arrowhead that flanks the Mississippi, sometimes to idyllic Painted Cave, deep down in the gullies of the southwest angle, sometimes to Lookout Point, the rocky pinnacle at the very tip of Wyalusing from which one looks up and down the

238

Looking north from the Wyalusing Camp Site. The Wisconsin lies 600 feet below in the foreground. In the middle distance Prairie du Chien is partly hidden by trees. The Iowa Mississippi bluffs swing across the distance.

A typical Wyalusing Road.

Looking up the Wisconsin from Wyalusing with the bridge at Bridgeport in the distance.

Signal Point, at the tip of the Wyalusing Wedge. The Wisconsin is
in the foreground, and beyond it the backwater of the Mississippi.
The Mississippi itself is barely visible as a light thread at the base
of the Iowa bluffs.

great Mississippi as well as far up into the Wisconsin's valley.

But at night, after supper, the conference was invariably held around an oak fire before the tent, on the very brink of the bluff.

In the gathering night the valleys of the two rivers became deep, dark depressions. Form faded from the earth. The only remaining form was the faintly etched line where bluffs met the sky, the pattern of lights in Prairie du Chien, three miles to the north, and over in McGregor, Iowa, in its niche of bluffs four miles to the west.

The night earth became more sound than form. There was the low, hushed whispering of the flowing river 600 feet below, the soft sighing of the age-old west wind in the trees, the crisp scratch of an October leaf falling, the barely audible swish of a lynx coming in for a closer investigation of our fire, of a raccoon climbing an oak to get a look at us, the soft splash of a fish, the rippling gurgle of a muskrat or otter swimming the river, and the far-off monotony of two whippoorwills that were behind their migration schedule. But the most stirring night sound was the whoo-whoo-whoo-whooooo of the great horned owl, repeated and answered and echoed all night long, an occasional silent interval terminated perhaps by the agonizing scream of a rabbit pounced upon by sharp talons, followed again by a deathly silence.

It was above the earth, in the heavens, that form reached its night intensity—in the vast awesomeness of millions of galaxies whirling in an overwhelming infinite space, certainly the most tremendous and superlatively beautiful spectacle man has ever seen.

The Milky Way, the galaxy in which our own earth spins its tiny orb, split the heavens grandly from northwest to southeast. Beyond our own galaxy millions of other galaxies blinked at us from millions of light years away.

Taurus hung over the eastern horizon at seven o'clock; Orion appeared at ten; Cerberus and Aquilla set at eleven; Andromeda was a little south of overhead at ten-thirty.

And there in the aromatic tang of the oak fire, the talk of the four days on the river was summarized and edited, everybody taking a good-natured part, serious and gay by turns, alternately talking and munching roasted chestnuts that were pulled out of the red fringe of glowing coals.

There is an essential element, a basic feeling of the unity of all nature including the brotherhood of all humanity, that is renewed when a person leaves the cities and returns to the woods and the trees, the soil and its grasses, to the hills and the rivers, and sits at night under the starlit sky.

Sitting there suspended in space, we had a grand sense of the timelessness of the universe in which a minute is a billion years, only to be reminded that even on timeless Wyalusing the fire had a way of burning down to coals, Orion and Taurus had a way of swinging across the heavens and down into the western horizon, the night had a way of fleeing when Homer's "rosy-fingered dawn" crept into the eastern sky.

Even there on Wyalusing we were rudely reminded that there are minutes, and that 60 minutes make an hour, that hours have a way of fleeing, and that there comes a time, after a wonderful evening of talk, to crawl into a sleeping bag, a time to start a new fire for breakfast eggs and ham, a time to take the canoes, and the girls, and the camp back home—back home where time runs in a finite human schedule.

Another Wyalusing Conference was at an end.